Fun for

ARMCHAIR DETECTIVES

JERRI WILLIAMS *and* **CHASE WERT**

FBI Word Search Puzzles: Fun for Armchair Detectives

The opinions expressed in this book are the author's and not those of the FBI.

Print ISBN: 978-1-7324624-8-9

Cover design by Teddi Black
Interior design by Megan McCullough

CONTENTS

FOREWORD

I'm a retired special agent who served with the FBI for 26-years. During a recent holiday visit, my adult son Chase Wert reminded me how I used to make word search puzzles to help him and his sisters learn their vocabulary words. He said the puzzles made learning fun. That's when and why I decided to create ***FBI Word Search Puzzles: Fun for Armchair Detectives***. Not only was it a chance to work on a project with my creative son, but the puzzle book fit with my mission to show the public who the FBI is and what the FBI does.

FBI Word Search Puzzles: Fun for Armchair Detectives provides an opportunity to investigate all aspects of the FBI while searching for words and terms with advanced FBI themes. Please note, many of the definitions used to introduce FBI programs and federal violations were obtained directly from the official FBI websites—FBI.gov and FBIJobs.gov. The bonus adult coloring pages are courtesy of images featured in the FBI photo gallery.

FBI Word Search Puzzles: Fun for Armchair Detectives is dedicated to Chase's daughter, my granddaughter, Wendy Odessa.

Jerri Williams

#1 WHAT THE FBI INVESTIGATES

The Federal Bureau of Investigation (FBI) is considered one of the top law enforcement agencies in the world. The agency, also known as The Bureau, is an intelligence-driven and threat-focused national security organization that investigates more than 300 violations of federal laws. A significant number of FBI investigations are conducted in concert with other law enforcement agencies or as part of joint task forces.

Locate and redact or circle the following words within the grid. The words may be hidden horizontally, vertically, or diagonally and may appear backward or forward. Ignore words contained within parentheses.

ART THEFT

BACKGROUND INVESTIGATIONS

BANK ROBBERY

CIVIL RIGHTS

COLOR OF LAW

COUNTERINTELLIGENCE

CRIMINAL ENTERPRISES

CRIMES AGAINST CHILDREN

CYBER CRIME

DOMESTIC TERRORISM

ECONOMIC CRIME

ENVIRONMENTAL CRIME

FRAUD

FUGITIVES

HATE CRIMES

HUMAN TRAFFICKING

IDENTITY THEFT

INDIAN COUNTRY

INTERNATIONAL TERRORISM

INTERSTATE THEFT

KIDNAPPINGS

ONLINE PREDATORS

ORGANIZED CRIME

PROPERTY CRIME

PUBLIC CORRUPTION

SERIAL MURDER

TRANSNATIONAL GANGS

VIOLENT CRIME

WHITE-COLLAR CRIME

WMD (Weapons of Mass Destruction)

#1 WHAT THE FBI INVESTIGATES

P S E T K Y G N I K C I F F A R T N A M U H J R R

M N M B F Q B J S R O T A D E R P E N I L N O T X

S O I W E N O I T P U R R O C C I L B U P K Y V X

I I R S M L I V M D U Q J I U Q N G V Q S U C M O

R T C G I I F V T C N G V B E J T N E S A C R S F

O A C N R Z J T P E S J A U C G E E G G E Y I I S

R G I I C H I G P M K N G S N B R N C N I B M R B

R I M P Y T A E J I K U P R E U S V H A O E I O W

E T O P T M I D V R G R M H G I T I C G R R N R A

T S N A R G Y J O C A E H A I D A R I L G C A R L

L E O N E B B B D R L D T T L E T O V A A R L E F

A V C D P H B R K A C R V E L N E N I N N I E T O

N N E I O E C X X L X U Q C E T T M L O I M N C R

O I T K R M L J O L F M E R T I H E R I Z E T I O

I D P Y P I M X F O U L Y I N T E N I T E F E T L

T N L I X R Z U S C G A A M I Y F T G A D C R S O

A U B A W C R X S E I I R E R T T A H N C Q P E C

N O N X M T G R L T T R T S E H J L T S R K R M F

R R X Q D N T V P I I E T U T E V C S N I R I O P

E G E X M E N V F H V S H J N F N R D A M B S D K

T K V W X L Y V R W E S E S U T B I H R E I E U L

N C W O Z O O R A D S E F F O X H M J T K N S A F

I A D R O I S O U K Y P T J C A S E X C W S O I V

S B A Y N V H R D J Y Y R T N U O C N A I D N I W

C R I M E S A G A I N S T C H I L D R E N N O M N

#2 FBI CORE VALUES AND HERALDRY OF THE FBI SEAL

The FBI's mission is to protect the American people and uphold the Constitution of the United States. Its core values guide how Bureau employees conduct themselves. The FBI seal, adopted in 1940, reflects the Bureau's mission and values. Each symbol and color in the seal has special significance.

Locate and redact or circle the following words within the grid. The words may be hidden horizontally, vertically, or diagonally and may appear backward or forward. Ignore words contained within parentheses.

ACADEMIC HONORS
ACCOUNTABILITY
BLUE FIELD
BRAVERY
CHALLENGES
CLEANLINESS
COMPASSION
COURAGE
DISTINCTION
DIVERSITY
ENFORCE CRIMINAL LAWS
FAIRNESS
FAME
FIDELITY
FORTY-SIX LEAVES
GOLD BEVELED EDGE
INTEGRITY
JUSTICE
LAUREL LEAF
LIGHT
NATIONAL SECURITY
PEACE
PERSONAL LEADERSHIP
PROFESSIONAL LEADERSHIP
PROTECT AMERICANS
RED STRIPES
RESPECT FOR DIGNITY
RUGGEDNESS
STRENGTH
THIRTEEN STARS
TRUTH
TWO BRANCHES
UNITY OF PURPOSE
UPHOLD THE CONSTITUTION
VALOR
VALUE
WHITE STRIPES

#2

FBI CORE VALUES AND HERALDRY OF THE FBI SEAL

M M G I T E G D E D E L E V E B D L O G P A T K P
N F Z U K P F E S N A C I R E M A T C E T O R P I
U X F P E S S E N I L N A E L C D X X S Y P X C H
P X Y T I R U C E S L A N O I T A N U U V I E Z S
H R E O Q R L F S E G N E L L A H C N N H H N C R
O D C Y S Y D O S Z F J T P V A L O R I T S F Z E
L Z I T Y T Y K W S O C I P I P T U R T G R O Y D
D W T I P I T S H E R F I G U Y H U Y Y N E R K A
T C S N M L I M I U T Z S J F T I O E O E D C M E
H D U G Y E L U T L Y Y R W O Y R M H F R A E B L
E L J I L D I L E A S T O C Q S T K F P T E C W L
C E N D I I B A S V I I N W M R E D Z U S L R R A
O I E R G F A U T A X R O S Y R E V A R B L I O N
N F I O H S T R R D L G H S G P N T D P I A M G O
S E D F T E N E I I E E C E V F S W I O N N I L S
T U X T U P U L P S A T I N V Q T O V S K O N U R
I L N C W I O L E T V N M D S I A B E E R I A E E
T B R E H R C E S I E I E E Q M R R R M S S L G P
U C L P F T C A V N S T D G U I S A S G R S L A W
T Y U S Y S A F U C M X A G T Y S N I B E E A R W
I G I E M D V M R T W Q C U Y Y W C T T M F W U L
O T U R I E P E A I M K A R S X O H Y B A O S O T
N O F U N R S T L O W H T U R T V E C T F R A C G
C O M P A S S I O N D M P S Y B B S N A S P P D U
S O L O L X T T E C A E P D R W F A I R N E S S L

#3 FBI JOBS

The FBI has a wide variety of career opportunities for individuals from all backgrounds, educational paths, and experiences.

Locate and redact or circle the following words within the grid. The words may be hidden horizontally, vertically, or diagonally and may appear backward or forward. Ignore words contained within parentheses.

ACCOUNTANT
ANALYST
ATTORNEY
AUDIO-VISUAL SPECIALIST
BIOLOGIST
BUDGET OFFICER
CHEMIST
CLERICAL STAFF
COMPUTER SCIENTIST
CRYPTOLOGIST
DOCUMENT ANALYST
EDITOR
ENGINEER
ELECTRONIC TECH
FINGERPRINT EXAMINER
FIREARMS EXPERT
FLEET MAINTENANCE
FORENSIC SCIENTIST
HUMAN RESOURCES
INSTRUCTOR
LEGAL ADVISOR
LINGUIST
MATHEMATICIAN
PARALEGAL
PHOTOGRAPHER
PILOT
POLICE OFFICER
PROJECT MANAGER
PUBLIC AFFAIRS
SCIENTIST
SOFTWARE DESIGNER
SPECIAL AGENT
SURVEILLANCE GROUP
WRITER

#3

FBI JOBS

N P T O W N F F A T S L A C I R E L C K J F U U K

E F W C R Y P T O L O G I S T T X T S I M E H C Y

H I O W U P Z P Y U D B W Q P S B F S G X F S F D

W U B A S H S O Z E D I T O R I G P M W Z L S E C

P B U A M O T L Q Y U T S M E T O T R Q A E E L T

R D O S Y T H I E E S U K S T N N N E V U E C E P

O O B G Y O O C O N O T A U I E R T E Q D T R C A

J C M A L G R E T R E S C R R I E S N L I M U T R

E U K E R R H O N O H I R V W C N Y I B O A O R A

C M Z F E A L F N T Q T E E F S I L G S V I S O L

T E M I N P G F L T H N C I Q C M A N G I N E N E

M N A R G H T I E A M E I L Q I A N E R S T R I G

A T T E I E S C G J P I F L R S X A V E U E C A

N A H A S R I E A T U C F A O N E E S X A N N T L

A N E R E N U R L S B S O N T E T C P T L A A E D

G A M M D S G A A I L R T C C R N D E S S N M C A

E L A S E E N C D T I E E E U O I C C I P C U H B

R Y T E R H I C V N C T G G R F R K I G E E H G F

A S I X A O L O I E A U D R T A P G A O C N A X J

H T C P W J F U S I F P U O S T R K L L I E E C N

T P I E T F Z N O C F M B U N O E K A O A Z E X H

H N A R F L C T R S A O R P I L G Z G I L X J A M

C R N T O D H A D H I C O G T I N Y E B I H Z V C

P I R F S H V N B J R C Y G N P I L N H S Q J H B

D S A W Q I B T S W S T L Z A H F R T J T M J I S

#4 FBI CORE COMPETENCIES

The Core Competencies of the FBI are the categories of knowledge, skills, and abilities all FBI employees are expected to cultivate and use in their work.

Locate and redact or circle the following words within the grid. The words may be hidden horizontally, vertically, or diagonally and may appear backward or forward. Ignore words contained within parentheses.

ACCEPT RESPONSIBILITY	IDENTIFY PROBLEMS	ORGANIZE
ADAPTABILITY	INITIATIVE	PERSONAL INTEGRITY
BE PROACTIVE	INSPIRE	PERSUADE
COLLABORATION	INTERPERSONAL ABILITY	PLAN
COMMUNICATION	JUDGMENT	POLITICAL SAVVY
DEVELOP SELF	LEADERSHIP	PRESENCE
DIRECT	LIAISE	PRIORITIZE
ESTABLISH RAPPORT	LISTEN AND INTERPRET	PROBLEM SOLVE
EVALUATE AND ANALYZE	MAKE DECISIONS	RESOLVE CONFLICT
FLEXIBILITY	MANAGE CHANGE	SENSITIVITY
FOLLOW THROUGH	MANAGE CONFLICT	SHOW RESPECT
IDENTIFY OPPORTUNITIES	MANAGE RISKS	SPEAK CLEARLY
	MENTOR	WRITE CLEARLY

#4 FBI CORE COMPETENCIES

U M E N T O R J U H H F Y R Y F E Y B Z X W E O Z
I J W Y V X X U T G J C A U T E V S A K H B S M L
A B E L P Z F D E U F T V C I F A N Y E V I I L I
S J V R W Q W G R O P G T Q L D L E C R S N A E D
U M I A A F B M P R Q U R Z I N U S L I V T I A E
M J T E P J E E R H D R B R B C A T U P D E L D N
O E A L E C P N E T Y M E J I E T A T S K R M E T
S G I C R G R T T W S C J N S Z E B X N S P E R I
M N T K S S O P N O T E M A N R A L O I K E E S F
E A I A O H A R I L N O A L O E N I K K S R Y H Y
L H N E N W C I D L C D N P P S D S W E I S T I O
B C I P A M T O N O O E A W S O A H Y V R O I P P
O E S S L M I R A F L V G R E L N R T L E N L T P
R G E O I A V I N H L E E I R V A A I O G A I C O
P A N R N K E T E P A L C T T E L P L S A L B E R
Y N S G T E S I T E B O O E P C Y P I M N A I P T
F A I A E D X Z S R O P N C E O Z O B E A B X S U
I M T N G E E E I S R S F L C N E R A L M I E E N
T Q I I R C V C L U A E L E C F Z T T B D L L R I
N R V Z I I O N N A T L I A A L W M P O A I F W T
E H I E T S M E H D I F C R T I L N A R M T E O I
D K T N Y I N S X E O N T L P C A R D P O Y Q H E
I N Y R M O R E O B N B N Y Z T T N A E Q R S S S
G G B D Q N K R N O I T A C I N U M M O C J A C I
K R T I J S D P P O L I T I C A L S A V V Y Z A X

#5 SPECIAL AGENT QUALIFICATION AND APPLICATION PROCESS

The Special Agent Selection System (SASS) is designed to identify the best candidates to become FBI Special Agents. Applicants must be between 23 and 36 years of age. Each candidate's suitability is assessed during a thorough background investigation. The process typically takes one year or longer to complete.

Locate and redact or circle the following words within the grid. The words may be hidden horizontally, vertically, or diagonally and may appear backward or forward. Ignore words contained within parentheses.

APPLICANT COORDINATOR
APPLICATION
ASSOCIATES
AVAILABILITY
BACHELOR'S DEGREE
BACKGROUND CHECK
BASIC REQUIREMENTS
CHARACTER
COLLEGE GRAD
COMPETITIVE
CONDITIONAL OFFER
CORE COMPETENCIES
DIVERSITY
DRIVER'S LICENSE
DRUG TEST
EXPERIENCE
FINANCIALLY RESPONSIBLE
FITNESS TEST
MEDICAL EXAM
MEET AND GREET
MILITARY WAIVER
PANEL INTERVIEW
PASSING SCORE
PERSONAL INTEGRITY
POLYGRAPH
QUALIFICATIONS
REPUTATION
RESUME
SECURITY CLEARANCE
SELECTION PROCESS
TESTING SITES
TRANSFER POLICY
WRITTEN EXAM
US CITIZEN

#5 SPECIAL AGENT QUALIFICATION AND APPLICATION PROCESS

S L R S X S B E T Y M L W E C N E I R E P X E O N

E Z E V U G B A C K G R O U N D C H E C K R Z G U

L Y F B C O R E C O M P E T E N C I E S Z E Z W T

E P F S S Y R N H G J E F A W O Q U P Z J V S X L

C D O Y N C T W N P A R R S R I M C A U L I E Z L

T A L G O I E U J U V S E E I T K H N S X A C V H

I R A O I L E S B G A O N T T A H A E Z E W U Q E

O G N E T O R C H Y I N O I T T P R L F A Y R S H

N E O R A P G I Q R L A I S E U A A I J I R I T A

P G I O C R D T E E A L T G N P R C N M K A T N F

R E T C I E N I H S B I A N E E G T T V G T Y E S

O L I S F F A Z C U I N C I X R Y E E A E I C M D

C L D G I S T E A M L T I T A W L R R S V L L E R

E O N N L N E N P E I E L S M A O Q V S I I E R I

S C O I A A E Y W D T G P E B I P K I O T M A I V

S R C S U R M W J Y Y R P T M E V G E C I Y R U E

E Q A S Q T M E F G N I A Q Z T U N W I T X A Q R

R O T A N I D R O O C T N A C I L P P A E D N E S

U P G P I G D D O A Y Y I H C L S D Z T P A C R L

T X K T S E T S S E N T I F W C W K R E M I E C I

N B O Y T I S R E V I D P D Z G E X X S O N Z I C

V A B Z O W X D E E R G E D S R O L E H C A B S E

F I N A N C I A L L Y R E S P O N S I B L E B A N

X W T T T Z T X M T S E T G U R D K X O V Q B S

N M I E H W H V F M M E D I C A L E X A M B Y X E

#6 FBI ACADEMY AND TRAINING

The FBI Academy is where New Agent Trainees and New Intelligence Analyst Trainees undergo basic field training, learning the essentials required to work in the field. It also functions as the world's premier law enforcement learning and research center and an advocate for law enforcement's best practices worldwide. The academy is located in Quantico, Virginia.

Locate and redact or circle the following words within the grid. The words may be hidden horizontally, vertically, or diagonally and may appear backward or forward. Ignore words contained within parentheses.

ACADEMICS

ARREST SCENARIOS

AUDITORIUM

BFTC (Basic Field Training Course)

CHAPEL

CLASSROOM

DEFENSE TACTICS

DINING HALL

DORM ROOMS

ETHICS

FIELD ASSIGNMENT

FIELD COUNSELOR

FIREARMS

FIRING RANGE

GRADUATION

HALL OF HONOR

HOGAN'S ALLEY

HOOVER ROAD

IN-SERVICE

LEGAL STUDIES

NARB (New Agent Review Board)

NAT (New Agent Trainee)

NATIONAL ACADEMY

NIAT (New Intelligence Analyst Trainee)

PHYSICAL FITNESS

PSYCHOLOGY

QUANTICO

ROLE PLAY

SURVIVAL SKILLS

TARGETS

TEVOC (Tactical Emergency Vehicle Operations Center)

TRAINING

TWENTY-ONE WEEKS

YELLOW BRICK ROAD

#6

FBI ACADEMY AND TRAINING

```
O H O O V E R R O A D C Q Z H O Q B H P M Q D G L
M P K K Z H C L A S S R O O M I O N B W R C S M E
P R G R A D U A T I O N R M V X J S C X C Y K R G
S X R E E M W K T G U C A K D A O O D P M G C X A
P R Y V E I J D X I M G T U X X R W Q K R O O N L
Q W B W K W B S X U D Z N F D I P M B A Z L V W S
A V C T M L T X N M E Y E I B I L C V B N O E U T
N Z C P L I U I D H K P V Q N O T R R N C H T O U
Y M E D A C A L A N O I T A N I L O R Y O C N F D
S G T V Y H A L L O F H O N O R A N R F U Y E I I
K K D A O R K C I R B W O L L E Y R O I F S M R E
E M W X G R K S C P T A I N Q C X I T N U P N I S
E F I E L D C O U N S E L O R I Q T K S I M G N Y
W Y J V A D E F E N S E T A C T I C S E O J I G S
E T H I C S N V S M O O R M R O D V Y R N Z S R A
N P D R U L W S V J B I M J K N I U U V L M S A P
O W Q W J W Y X X H R D C W T E S Z Z I Z M A N G
Y C A U S D I N I N G H A L L B A C I C A N D G B
T A R R E S T S C E N A R I O S D N I E B N L E L
N S U R V I V A L S K I L L S T A M U M L O E Y V
E B R A N Y B J F J M Q I I U T U Z F M E V I W E
W H S M R A E R I F W P X R O L E P L A Y D F K G
T O Y E L L A S N A G O H B S T E G R A T O A L Z
R E O C I T N A U Q O L N L E Y L M S N S R E C G
I C H A P E L S S E N T I F L A C I S Y H P B H A
```

#7 PHYSICAL FITNESS TEST

Special Agents must be mentally and physically prepared for their work. The FBI requires every applicant to pass the Physical Fitness Test (PFT) before receiving an appointment and beginning training at the FBI Academy.

Locate and redact or circle the following words within the grid. The words may be hidden horizontally, vertically, or diagonally and may appear backward or forward. Ignore words contained within parentheses.

APPLICATION PROCESS	OVAL TRACK	SELF ASSESSMENT
CONTINUOUS MOTION	PASSING SCORE	SIT UPS
CROSS TRAINING	PEAK CONDITION	SPRINT
CUMULATIVE SCORE	PFT	STOPWATCH
DEAD HANG	PREPAREDNESS	TERMINATION
EXERCISE PROTOCOLS	PULL UPS	TESTING APP
HEALTH AND FITNESS	PUSH UPS	TIMED EXERCISES
INTERVALS	READINESS	TRAINING INTENSITY
MAXIMUM SCORE	RECOVERY	TWELVE POINTS
MILE AND A HALF RUN	REPETITIONS	
MIND-MUSCLE INTERACTION	SELECTION PROCESS	

#7 PHYSICAL FITNESS TEST

X E S E L E C T I O N P R O C E S S L T E W G X N

E W P E B K S U B S P U T I S S P W S Q Q H S T O

J G X C T W G Z R B M F R K A L C V E T R C P V I

S S E N D E R A P E R P Z W P A H R L R S S H A T

C Z D T F P M P M S P K X Z P V E E F A H L E Q A

P M Z Y M D I A T Q F N B Z L R O S A I W O A T N

M Z G J S U N S I H T W Y V I E C W S N T C L R I

Y A E W M Y D S M H F K N K C T U H S I S O T E M

F X L L C T M I E R X Q U Z A N M X E N Y T H A R

S N U L N J U N D T O D R C T I U T S G E O A D E

P O I E N Q S G E K S Q F I I C L R S I N R N I T

D I V J V T C S X E T E L Y O C A Z M N C P D N G

E T D R N S L C E G N S A U N W T R E T W E F E E

R I Q P M N E O R N I T H S P V I D N E X S I S G

O D A U M O I R C A O O A S R Z V Q T N V I T S G

C N F S R I N E I H P P D P O P E D O S Z C N J Y

S O S H D T T R S D E W N U C E S M C I B R E V D

M C P U R I E Q E A V A A L E U C R F T N E S X R

U K R P E T R D S E L T E L S O O R W Y Y X S E L

M A I S C E A C J D E C L U S H R A Y A X E Q I R

I E N M O P C F M U W H I P N I E B W L X W F Y P

X P T S V E T H Z M T P M W D P P A G N I T S E T

A K U S E R I O V N O I T O M S U O U N I T N O C

M F B C R U O G N I N I A R T S S O R C F Z L A S

I L W P Y F N Q Z N O V A L T R A C K H P W K R I

#8 FIELD OFFICES (A THRU L)

The FBI has 56 field offices (also called divisions) centrally located in major metropolitan areas across the US and Puerto Rico. Within these field offices are a total of about 380 resident agencies (RAs) located in smaller cities and towns. Agents assigned to field offices and RAs work closely with their local, state, and federal law enforcement counterparts within the division's territory.

Locate and redact or circle the following words within the grid. The words may be hidden horizontally, vertically, or diagonally and may appear backward or forward. Ignore words contained within parentheses.

ALBANY
ALBUQUERQUE
ANCHORAGE
ATLANTA
BALTIMORE
BIRMINGHAM
BOSTON
BUFFALO
CHARLOTTE
CHICAGO
CINCINNATI
CLEVELAND
COLUMBIA
DALLAS
DENVER
DETROIT
EL PASO
HONOLULU
HOUSTON
INDIANAPOLIS
JACKSON
JACKSONVILLE
KANSAS CITY
KNOXVILLE
LAS VEGAS
LITTLE ROCK
LOS ANGELES
LOUISVILLE

#8 FIELD OFFICES (A THRU L)

U B N B J B L J D I X K N O X V I L L E P Q I D Z

G N A T E L P A S O O B W Y F D N A L E V E L C T

S H U D A P T J T C G Z S Y M E B X C D I X E K J

A L B U Q U E R Q U E X S D D N B T F P V Q G C J

D P Z I I W H S I L O P A N A I D N I O A T A O H

U C H J Z Y V H O N O L U L U M C K U X X K R R W

M F H J Z X Q D B O I P B P A U E H B J I E O E L

J A G S A U S G T T G O F H S L O L V Q Z O H L D

C D S N Y C U A X J B U G J L L P C S Z N M C T L

Z P F R W R K K L V A N C I W M I D Y R C U N T O

F B H Q E N H S X L I W V W S N Y X A D Q Z A I S

P Y J V Q J J M O M A S F E C T X N V L X K F L A

C D N H Q J Q R R N I D W I T Y R S I U B E L X N

W E M X X F P I A U S B N L T T W O S Z M A Z M G

D Q Q V Q M B H O I U N X B K Y O R A R B I N Z E

Q J A O S N A L M F A C O F Q U D L D Y F S W Y L

D N P G H A J E F T O Z D F B A K B R U G T J C E

Z Z Q A D T G A I B H C O L U M B I A A H R N U S

X L S C Z E L E N O S O S B O S T O N G H E L N W

H A N I U O O A V X K P U D S X N K V F C C N B F

G T I H B G N G N S A D X S O Y T I C S A S N A K

L T V C S O N C N X A M W P T G G A D X N E R K H

Q O R M N A U J K M F L E L T O A T L A N T A O D

R O B A L T I M O R E K N I T X N T U Z N C Q M Y

G D T I O R T E D E D E L L I V N O S K C A J H A

#9 FIELD OFFICES (M THRU Z)

The FBI has 56 field offices (also called divisions) centrally located in major metropolitan areas across the U.S. and Puerto Rico. Within these field offices are a total of about 380resident agencies (RAs) located in smaller cities and towns. Agents assigned to field offices and RAs work closely with their local, state, and federal law enforcement counterparts within the division's territory.

Locate and redact or circle the following words within the grid. The words may be hidden horizontally, vertically, or diagonally and may appear backward or forward. Ignore words contained within parentheses.

MEMPHIS
MIAMI
MILWAUKEE
MINNEAPOLIS
MOBILE
NEWARK
NEW HAVEN
NEW ORLEANS
NEW YORK
NORFOLK
OKLAHOMA CITY
OMAHA
PHILADELPHIA
PHOENIX
PITTSBURGH
PORTLAND
RICHMOND
SACRAMENTO
SALT LAKE CITY
SAN ANTONIO
SAN DIEGO
SAN FRANCISCO
SAN JUAN
SEATTLE
SPRINGFIELD
ST. LOUIS
TAMPA
WASHINGTON DC

#9 FIELD OFFICES (M THRU Z)

K U M Q N O K L A H O M A C I T Y F I P O V G Q B
P T O P I T T S B U R G H J Q X A P M A T R U T D
U V C Q C Y U J W A S H I N G T O N D C G E S G K
H Z H B N A J E L Q E G D W O C S R H M R I N Q Q
R U K P F R T M L E A L I I J R G K I V D D E T K
S D P Z U Z F C K T N B U N J Q F T P E L A W W O
S M I J Q Y Q U U S T E U N T M H O Y Q E I H N C
I P G Y O F A L V G A A W L Q K F Y L Y I H A S S
L P Q F M W J V D K T N E A T M U E G K F P V G I
O T V D L D Z U N J V M D S R B Y L R B G L E X C
P K Z I N K V E O W V E E I V K B M G R N E N F N
A R M M E B K L M G O Z S M E V G B Z E I D I T A
E O O H A S T I H M U F B Z P G I L C X R A T R R
N Y X H P X R B C A O E C C E H O E S X P L H J F
N W W R M K G O I U L O Y S S Y I A Z I S I L Y N
I E C X V B P M R E R O L C O S L S V N P H R I A
M N Q Y S C Q Y R R Y G I J X T F S B E I P C F S
Z S A C R A M E N T O E J C L R O E F O M C B H R
B P Y G S A N J U A N J B A Z M G J I H A E F E C
I N E W O R L E A N S V K H A R G K N P I Q P P N
Z N G N X N X K Z X Q E K H D N D S U T M X V Y F
Z I I X L U X E L Z C I A T K O T S L V G V E F S
L E E D R T W S U I O U N X E S A N A N T O N I O
A C C N U L Q B T K C O Z B I C D N A L T R O P P
C A U Q X S G Y R F S I U O L T S L O H O E Q A V

#10 IN THE FIELD OFFICE

FBI agents and professional support staff assigned to the field report to field offices located throughout the United States. These field offices, also known as divisions, are open 24 hours a day, every day of the year. They are where investigations are conducted and administrative and case management duties are performed.

Locate and redact or circle the following words within the grid. The words may be hidden horizontally, vertically, or diagonally and may appear backward or forward. Ignore words contained within parentheses. Ignore words contained within parentheses.

AVP (Availability Pay)

BULLPEN

CASE FILES

CASELOAD

CLOSED FILES

COMMAND CENTER

CONFERENCE ROOMS

EVIDENCE VAULT

FBIRA STORE (FBI Recreation Association)

FEDERAL BUILDING

FILE REVIEW

FITNESS CENTER

GUN VAULT

HEADQUARTER CITY

HUMINT FILES (Human Intelligence)

INTELLIGENCE ANALYSTS

INTERVIEW ROOMS

LOBBY

MAHOGANY ROW

MOST WANTED DISPLAY

MUG ROOM

POLYGRAPH ROOM

PROFESSIONAL STAFF

RECEPTION

RESIDENT AGENCY

SAC OFFICE (Special Agent in Charge)

SCIF (Sensitive Compartmented Information Facility)

SPECIAL AGENTS

SQUAD AREA

STAFFING LEVELS

STANDALONE SITE

SUPERVISOR OFFICE

SUPPLY ROOM

SWITCHBOARD

WALL OF HONOR

#10

IN THE FIELD OFFICE

```
Y S T S Y L A N A E C N E G I L L E T N I T F C G
I A K P O S T N E G A L A I C E P S B L Z L D X D
M O S T W A N T E D D I S P L A Y T H J E U E S Y
R E T N E C D N A M M O C S S A T P E C R A C M B
O B T Z C A S E L O A D P U S E R M A E O V I O T
D S P Y I Q I D C Y L N R P D R E O D N T N F O S
S M C V I Q G R A H S E O P X A T O Q S S U F R O
H W W I A K X A S V D C F L O D N R U M A G O W E
O B F S F L U O E Y N I E Y Q A E H A O R N R E O
E I I V S U F B F B W F S R Q U C P R O I T O I M
S W L X T V M H I H U F S O P Q S A T R B R S V U
T O E M A T G C L C Y O I O S S S R E E F E I R G
A R R W N L C T E N V C O M X J E G R C P C V E R
F Y E A D U L I S L A A N H R K N Y C N D E R T O
F N V L A A O W P T E S A T G L T L I E C P E N O
I A I L L V S S N E P L L U B Q I O T R J T P I M
N G E O O E E A E K Q I S B U X F P Y E W I U H R
G O W F N C D L S U B J T L M F T A P F Y O S J U
L H F H E N F Y T C B I A A E L P S I N K N G A N
E A R O S E I C B L J T F R W Y C J V O Z W X I K
V M F N I D L B W B D I F R V N H M A C D C S Y E
E M S O T I E B Y E O O P C I U Z R N B I N G H C
L J K R E V S X E A H L S E L I F T N I M U H Y C
S G Y C N E G A T N E D I S E R R T W K L Q M E W
K G Q L T U N G N I D L I U B L A R E D E F R E Z
```

#11 FBI FIELD GEAR

FBI agents spend most days gathering information and evidence. Here are some of the items they wear, use, and carry.

Locate and redact or circle the following words within the grid. The words may be hidden horizontally, vertically, or diagonally and may appear backward or forward. Ignore words contained within parentheses.

AMMO
BADGE
BALLISTIC VEST
BASEBALL CAP
BRIEFCASE
BULLETS
BUREAU CAR
BUSINESS CARDS
CASE FILE
CASUAL CLOTHES
CELL PHONE
CREDENTIALS
DARK SUIT
FBI SEAL
FLEX CUFFS
GLOCK
GYM BAG
HANDCUFFS
HANDHELD RADIO
HOLSTER
INK PEN
LAPTOP
LEATHER CASE
NOTEBOOK
PEPPER SPRAY
RAID JACKET
SPEED LOADER
TACTICAL PANTS

#11

FBI FIELD GEAR

I Q D X S F F U C D N A H Y Z A R O X J N W B Y T
F Z B V B B O X O F F X O Y A R P S R E P P E P Z
S L A L O A S C H V B Z B N M Y V G U H S N P I T
F X L V T S K O O B E T O N P S T A C M S S W M X
Y W L I W L J X V A O C S Y T K Y B F B K E K R G
R E I Z C E L L P H O N E T J S D M I W P H V P L
X V S C K J R D Y B A D G E E V J Y X H R T U W H
V X T R K I M U Q H R J M T F L P G Z K S O M M V
P N I E V K G L V X U X H P V W L M Z E N L S D R
H N C D T A R E T S L O H E K T G U K M O C D F I
B R V E I C B A B A Y S N U B W X J B C Z L R G E
G I E N V P R N B T U F W S P N H I B G U A A E S
L E S T R A I X E L D S O A E Z Z H M K E U C K T
O G T I E C E K X N N Q O I L I N K P E N S S U N
C F I A D L F J F F L Z Q C I E Y C B T F A S D A
K T Z L A L C A U U X J I K F C B Y E T H C E O P
P E P S O A A J P G A U I I E V N Z R J B F N G A
I K E F L B S R O R M T I U S K R A D J U N I P C
T C N B D E E X T V M A Y C A D N U W V R Q S I I
N A S I E S M K P U O Q F H C V F A C E E U U W T
H J M S E A K T A Y W B M K T J G S A E A V B O C
P D X E P B V M L E G O X K M R R V Y U U I G F A
I I M A S B R H A N D H E L D R A D I O C M L F T
C A R L L K N G L E A T H E R C A S E R A K L N G
Z R S F F U C X E L F K D G V W O J K V R O V P X

#12 CAREER PATHS AND POSITIONS

Because of the FBI's mission to protect the American people, effective leadership is essential. Whether they are managing cases, squads, programs, or entire offices and divisions, employees are encouraged to view leadership development as a continuous cycle, from their first day on the job to the day they retire. Career advancement may require frequent transfers between the field and FBI Headquarters.

Locate and redact or circle the following words within the grid. The words may be hidden horizontally, vertically, or diagonally and may appear backward or forward. Ignore words contained within parentheses.

ADIC (Assistant Director in Charge)

ASSISTANT DIRECTOR

ASSOCIATE DEPUTY DIRECTOR

CAREER BOARD

CAREER DEVELOPMENT

CHAIN OF COMMAND

CHIEF INFORMATION OFFICER

CHIEF OF STAFF

DAD (Deputy Assistant Director)

DEPUTY DIRECTOR

DIRECTOR

EAD (Executive Assistant Director)

GENERAL COUNSEL

GRADUATION

HEADQUARTER SUPERVISOR

INSPECTOR

JOB POSTINGS

LOCALITY PAY

MANDATORY RETIREMENT

OFFICE OF PREFERENCE

OMBUDSMAN

OPR (Office of Professional Responsibility)

PAY SCALE

POST-FBI JOB

RELIEF SUPERVISOR

SAC (Special Agent in Charge)

SECTION CHIEF

SES (Senior Executive Service)

SPECIAL AGENT

SSA (Supervisory Special Agent)

STREET AGENT

TRANSFERS

UNIT CHIEF

#12 CAREER PATHS AND POSITIONS

```
F J G B H E A D Q U A R T E R S U P E R V I S O R
K U U U I V D N A M M O C F O N I A H C X J H Y H
P M G W B D O A F G E N E R A L C O U N S E L R R
X Z T S A V A U F V S C D C G I J N V H T Q O E Q
A X S F D N W D U H F L E Y L D E E I N C T C R B
D U A Z I N P C R F V F I Y E E X I E G C I G N J
I P C A R E T F W G N O A P D U R M T E F C B O Q
C S E S E A Z X Y F R P U R L B E I R F D A O I S
A R V O C D H B O Z Y T A B O R V I O S F R J T R
U O P I T I L F O T Y O L T I Y D N V K X E I A E
O T W H O A J Y I D B F N T X Y O F X G S E B U F
O C F F R S Y L I R U E E T T I O R R E O R F D S
N E F W B S A R E L G R N U T M E O C I Q D T A N
X R G G M C E E X A Y E P A B E F T K Q T E S R A
F I H P O C R D L R G E M U I X I C M I O V O G R
B D D L T A D A O A D R D N L O W E O W L E P P T
F T O O C V I T T E O S D R N Y T P B P Y L R P S
E N R Z C C A E T F M I U C O E O S J Y R O J A W
I A Y O E D E A N A D P H H M T T N U Q A P S Y Q
H T W P N R I I N U P I N I V C K I G U I M M S S
C S S A T C F C H I E F O F S T A F F I O E I C W
T I M S O E M X C F S P H A B R H H F W B N Y A J
I S S S I R O S I V R E P U S F E I L E R T X L T
N S S H P J O B P O S T I N G S A A D H M S T E U
U A C O F F I C E O F P R E F E R E N C E D O D E
```

#13 INTERVIEW TECHNIQUES

Agents take copious notes during interviews and then produce an FD-302 report of interview, a written narrative. Each encounter with a subject, victim, or witness is an opportunity for an FBI agent to build rapport and an alliance with valuable and knowledgeable sources in the criminal world. Therefore, although obtaining a confession is the primary purpose of interviewing a subject in custody, the secondary goal is to obtain cooperation.

Locate and redact or circle the following words within the grid. The words may be hidden horizontally, vertically, or diagonally and may appear backward or forward. Ignore words contained within parentheses.

BAD COP	INFORMANTS	RAPPORT
BODY LANGUAGE	INNOCENT	RATIONALIZE
COERCE	INTELLIGENCE	RESPECT
CONFESSION	INTERROGATE	SECRETS
COOPERATION	INTERVIEW	STRESS
DEBRIEF	LAWYER	SUBJECT
EMPATHIZE	MOTIVATE	TECHNIQUES
FACT FINDING	NEGOTIATION	VALIDATION
FLIP	NONVERBAL CUES	WITNESS
GOOD COP	OBSERVE	
GUILTY	POLYGRAPH	

#13

INTERVIEW TECHNIQUES

X B G H T Y W E F T Y P I W X N O I T A D I L A V

Y U Y F C V E T P M T E C R E O C X R V U R T Q H

T M L O E S I G Z G N E G O T I A T I O N D C S C

N F O N P E V M E L S D R P U V Q V U D D O E E M

T D M O S L R F M V D W H F R V R C C S S F J U K

Y N G T E E E K P C R O Y S Y Q V O T X T D B Q V

R R E Z R B T Q A D I E B P D M L O V Y E S U I C

K K W C X K N K T B W A S Y Q T G P M B R G S N O

H O A Z O L I S H E D I U B U Y R E P G C N H H P

D C T G O N K I I A F E T K O H P R Z O E I C C Z

K B O O O F N W Z V Y G B N J F Q A S O S D I E B

Z S U U K V N I E Z Z Y Q R E F G T E D I N N T P

C O N F E S S I O N S V T C I S V I U C I I T K W

D B S K G H V Z E F E S E Y G E S O C O N F E L I

S M U O H M L C P T G Q Z X I Y F N L P T T R A N

O F G L Q D V I R R A C I P H T C Z A E E C R W F

G P F D A T L L N O U H L C P X F B B T L A O Y O

E U U I Z F U M E P G J A M A S C O R A L F G E R

O O I B X H D C T P N S N P R S G H E V I B A R M

X L V L Q M H B K A A L O S G I M R V I G I T C A

P S N W T C O L E R L K I T Y P A Y N T E V E M N

I P C C R Y S P S O Y V T R L G V N O O N E C T T

L P U Z D A B V D S D Q A E O S B F N M C Q N M S

O B W F J Z Q N X D O S R S P Q H B H C E Q E K D

V I I N H Y Z C X R B I F S S J Y C G P O C D A B

#14 ELECTRONIC SURVEILLANCE

The FBI collects evidence and intelligence through the interception of cable-connected, wireless, and data networks. An FBI agent must first receive administrative or court authorization before accessing and monitoring wire, oral, or electronic communications. Before a federal judge will consider authorization of a wiretap, a detailed application must be submitted establishing the facts of the investigation and the underlying alleged felony offense, probable cause that a felony has occurred or will occur, and information supporting the belief that the wiretap may provide additional evidence of the violation of federal law.

Locate and redact or circle the following words within the grid. The words may be hidden horizontally, vertically, or diagonally and may appear backward or forward. Ignore words contained within parentheses.

CAMERA

CONSENSUAL

COOPERATING WITNESS

COURT AUTHORIZED

COURT ORDER

COVERT

DATABASE

DIGITAL RECORDER

EVIDENCE

ELECTRONIC

FBI VAN

FISA ORDER (Foreign Intelligence Surveillance Act)

INFILTRATE

INFORMANT

INSTALLATION

INTERCEPT

MICROPHONE

MINIMIZATION

MONITOR

PEN REGISTER

RECORDING EQUIPMENT

SENSITIVE

SURREPTITIOUS ENTRY

SURVEILLANCE SQUAD

TECH AGENT

TITLE III

TRACKING DEVICES

TRANSMITTER

TRAP AND TRACE

UNDERCOVER AGENT

VIDEO

WIRETAP

#14 ELECTRONIC SURVEILLANCE

A S C R E C N E D I V E J V D S P A T E R I W V T
H D A N Y S E C I V E D G N I K C A R T T E S E R
S U R V E I L L A N C E S Q U A D U K S E C E L A
Z P Q Q T N E G A H C E T P Y E S A B A T A D E N
O O O W V P E N R E G I S T E R P R X L A R F C S
T N E M P I U Q E G N I D R O C E R J Y Q T W T M
G R F E T A R T L I F N I L S W V F B S C D S R I
W S U R R E P T I T I O U S E N T R Y B D N R O T
M A U X P D I N F O R M A N T H K H K W B A E N T
H R P S S E N T I W G N I T A R E P O O C P D I E
B C O U R T A U T H O R I Z E D U O I T Y A R C R
N K E X C T U N D E R C O V E R A G E N T R O J N
N O E T W E N O H P O R C I M V W I A O E T C O O
B A I S Z G X B W V N N A L Q I E V N H F T E B I
W X V T W U T R G O N A E R Z D I L M S P N R P T
U I R M A C R D E B G F V B E B N L S E H O L D A
M I H Q G Z O E E D Y F A J F M N V C Q O O A K L
Z I E T P Q I N D Y R N N O S W A R O Q E Z T S L
S E C V R S Q M S R W O Q E V M E C J R D P I R A
C L Q F Q E R K I E O B A J W T C J B P I X G P T
U T S O Z M V I H N N T S S N C Z R U V V I I C S
G I G Y W M C O Q X I S R I I Y O Q I G S J D P N
G T S O B U V S C C J M U U V F X C Q Z P G B T I
V C D T L M D U P K W Z A A O E V I T I S N E S Z
T K L C G G I L O W N Q E O L C H Y R O T I N O M

#15 PHYSICAL SURVEILLANCE

FBI surveillance teams operating in the US covertly track drug dealers, corrupt officials, spies, terrorists, and other criminals. Acting as the eyes and ears of the FBI, agents and surveillance professionals follow subjects on foot, in cars, and on public transportation to identify subjects and gather evidence.

Locate and redact or circle the following words within the grid. The words may be hidden horizontally, vertically, or diagonally and may appear backward or forward. Ignore words contained within parentheses.

AIRPLANE
BELOW THE RADAR
CHANGE OF CLOTHES
CLANDESTINE
CLEAN TRACKS
COVER STORY
COVERT
DIRECT OBSERVATION
DISGUISES
DRONE
EYEBALL
FBI VAN
FOLLOW
FOOT SURVEILLANCE
GHOSTS
GPS TRACKER
INFRARED
MOBILE COMMAND
NEIGHBORHOOD CANVASS
NIGHT VISION
OFF-SITE
ON THE MOVE
OUT OF POCKET
PHOTOGRAPHY
POLE CAMERA
PULLBACK
SOG (Special Operations Group)
SSG (Special Surveillance Group)
STAKEOUT
STATIONARY
SURVEILLANCE LOG
TARGET
THERMAL IMAGING
UNDETECTED
VEHICLE SURVEILLANCE

#15 PHYSICAL SURVEILLANCE

```
C O V E R S T O R Y K E C S P E E B D I E I S K I
R F V C J W N O I S I V T H G I N Y N N K C E Z Q
V W N T P J T W T G G H O S T S R F A C C Y H U U
E K O H J M U T L T T V Q Z G V R L F O A Y T Z Q
H E I E Z O P O L E C A M E R A P X D V B T O H M
I J T R F W T H K U M J P N R R H V G E L I L H Q
C K A M O F U J B E A X I E I E O S N R L Y C U Q
L M V A O Y O F W E G P D A N F S H K T U P F L I
E A R L T D E P Q H L X C I Q C J N P J P O O Z T
S J E I S E K S O G V O T I L O U I Q E Z K E K Q
U A S M U F A F D A G S W E U N T A D W H R G G P
R W B A R B T E H Z E J A T D T V I H V V D N Y P
V H O G V I S C S D W N E E H H E E G Q W E A H O
E W T I E V M I N H T Y T U Q E O W X B T M H P U
I O C N I A S A M R E E L X A M R B O I I T C A T
L T E G L N L J A B C E I X R O N A S Q I G W R O
L E R S L C D C A T N L Q S Z V R F D Y R O O G F
A G I F A T K L E O L Y T Q A E F P Q A L G Z O P
N R D D N S L D R D R I D N E O L Q H L R Z G T O
C A P F C Y A D Y Z N U Y J N J O I O L O G Q O C
E T Y A E S E S I U G S I D B H O F A U H P L H K
N M S S A V N A C D O O H R O B H G I E N B G P E
G P S T R A C K E R G N Y R A N O I T A T S V S T
V P C P C M A T P H D N A M M O C E L I B O M T U
B Q E G O L E C N A L L I E V R U S Z J Y E H Q X
```

#16 FIREARMS OF THE FBI

The FBI was given federal authority to carry firearms in 1934. In the gun vault at the FBI Academy, the FBI keeps a collection of more than 7,000 weapons and gun parts. Analysts use these items to match ballistics and to rebuild destroyed weapons needed for evidence.

Locate and redact or circle the following words within the grid. The words may be hidden horizontally, vertically, or diagonally and may appear backward or forward. Ignore words contained within parentheses.

AMMUNITION
BALLISTICS
BOLT-ACTION
BROWNING
CALIBER
CARTRIDGES
COLT
CYLINDER
DRUM MAGAZINE
FIREARMS COLLECTION
GLOCK
GRENADE LAUNCHER
GRIP ADAPTERS
HANDGUN
MACHINE GUN
MAGAZINE
MAGNUM
PISTOL
PUMP-ACTION
REMINGTON
REVOLVER
RIFLES
SCOPE
SEMI-AUTOMATIC
SERIAL NUMBER
SHOTGUN
SHOTGUN SHELLS
SHOULDER WEAPON
SIG SAUER
SMITH AND WESSON
SUBMACHINE GUN
THOMPSON
TWELVE GAUGE
WINCHESTER

#16 FIREARMS OF THE FBI

L Q G W G J S Y V P X R E B M U N L A I R E S P P
H N E R X Q N O P A E W R E D L U O H S H O E Q L
B Z M F J S H O T G U N Z H H I M K S H E K T J S
U S U B M A C H I N E G U N S H A N D G U N U H R
O N O I T C E L L O C S M R A E R I F W U O J E H
S G Z V G V H W N R E D N I L Y C P V H Q H D X V
W N N L W R E T S E H C N I W S E G D I R T R A C
Y V O J Y Q U I Y S H O T G U N S H E L L S I O L
Y C C A U S R E T P A D A P I R G E S L I D X W D
K Z L E Z R E H C N U A L E D A N E R G O Q A X A
S E M I A U T O M A T I C W I P U M P A C T I O N
J W W M U N G A M B E B Y X R E M I N G T O N E N
A J J N H M A G A Z I N E J T C L R I F L E S E O
J E N I Z A G A M M U R D T W E L V E G A U G E S
Z B R K M P N O S P M O H T M U T H H Q E P O C S
K B U Q I X H Q H H E Z B A L L I S T I C S R C E
P B C S Q S F X X M W M I H R E L O R G F Q W J W
Y R T H S Q L L M E W F Z K E O V K V B O J J E D
O O O L J S W C P B Z J V T V Q U X C R T T M L N
L W I Z N O I T I N U M M A L H J X Q E L Q E V A
E N R G M F K S G G S P K O O V G Q O B O V F P H
Y I Z U X X R E U A S G I S V V O H C I C M C F T
X N N U G E N I H C A M T W E H C I N L F B R V I
B G X B T E A S I U K O X F R W J O J A V K E U M
P J M V Z Y N G I Z O H D T B O L T A C T I O N S

#17 FIREARMS TRAINING

Firearms training is more than marksmanship. When agents learn about how and when to use their weapons, they also learn and understand the ramifications of the use of deadly force. New agents shoot more than four thousand rounds at the FBI Academy. In the field, agents must qualify four times a year with the pistol and rifle.

Locate and redact or circle the following words within the grid. The words may be hidden horizontally, vertically, or diagonally and may appear backward or forward. Ignore words contained within parentheses.

AMMO
AVAILABLE COVER
BODY ARMOR
BRASS
BULLSEYE
CLAY PIGEONS
CONTROL TOWER
DEADLY FORCE
DRY FIRE
FIRING LINE
FTU (Firearms Training Unit)
GUN CLEANING ROOM
GUN VAULT
HOLLOW POINT
HOT LINE
ISOSCELES POSITION
NIGHT FIRE
PFI (Principal Firearms Instructor)
PISTOL COURSE
POSSIBLE CLUB
QUALIFY
RANGE
RED HANDLE
SCOPE
SCORE
SERVICE ROUND
SHOOTER
SILHOUETTE TARGET
SIMULATOR
SIMUNITION ROUNDS
SITES
SLUGS
SPEED LOADER
TRIGGER PULL
WEAK HAND SHOOTING
YARD LINE

#17

FIREARMS TRAINING

```
A P O S S I B L E C L U B W J K Y A R D L I N E R
J E B M R W C L A Y P I G E O N S U E O S X A Y E
V M I S O S C E L E S P O S I T I O N R W F F T D
C E S Y K Y F R S V I S B I W D F E Z W Q T W R H
M N R F Q Y L I W Z E V A O R R Q E G N A R H R A
G Q O I L S E C I F K A X R D E T R M U G L I C N
P E G S F U L Z U J V W E M B Y T F N X M T M F D
B H U S O T E U H V P B S R J E A O X J I N O S L
N N N W O R H V G H S I T E S M B R O X V J O H E
V E V T P E E G Q S N L W W E Y B R M H L R R O H
D W A Z F Z F J I N P W H R G Y U R W O S M   L Q
P S U F S A G Q R N R Q Q D V V U T Y K R Q G L S
E N L F W E A K H A N D S H O O T I N G R O N O I
T F T U P C O N T R O L T O W E R Y K G F F I W M
F I R I N G L I N E E R I F Y R D U B U O Q N P U
S I M U N I T I O N R O U N D S X E Z T Z U A O L
J O T E G R A T E T T E U O H L I S R F W A E I A
Z T L V M D E A D L Y F O R C E E W H F I L L N T
C A V A I L A B L E C O V E R J H S A R Z I C T O
U L A T S E R V I C E R O U N D C O H K K F N Y R
E P O C S B U F W U K R V Z N O U O T A U Y U Z D
T R I G G E R P U L L T N Y R Z W S R L N O G G E
E E S R U O C L O T S I P E N I V P K M I P M U K
S P E E D L O A D E R B H I C W F O N C W N G M D
Y B U L L S E Y E A M X Z T L I L B J C R P E P A
```

#18

FBI IN MOVIES

What most people know about the FBI comes from books, TV, and movies. Some films and fiction feature an accurate portrayal of the FBI, while others are not so successful.

Locate and redact or circle the following words within the grid. The words may be hidden horizontally, vertically, or diagonally and may appear backward or forward. Ignore words contained within parentheses.

ABOVE SUSPICION
AMERICAN HUSTLE
BLACK MASS
BREACH
CATCH ME IF YOU CAN
(The) COMPANY YOU KEEP
CORKY ROMANO
DONNIE BRASCO
FACE/OFF
(The) FBI STORY
(The) FIRM
HANNIBAL
HEAT
IMPERIUM
(The) INFORMANT
J. EDGAR
(The) KINGDOM
(The) LAST SHOT
MARK FELT
MISS CONGENIALITY
PATRIOTS DAY
PUBLIC ENEMIES
RED DRAGON
RICHARD JEWELL
SHOOTER
SICARIO
(The) SIEGE
(The) SILENCE OF THE LAMBS
SURVEILLANCE
(The) TOWN
TRAITOR
UNTHINKABLE
UNTRACEABLE
WIND RIVER
(The) WOLF OF WALL STREET

#18

FBI IN MOVIES

D M R I C H A R D J E W E L L U E J X N B Y O H K
O C S P R C R L G N G L A S T S H O T Y L Q G G V
R R D N H W L M B M L I M P E R I U M A A D V Y D
O Y C O C Q V U T E U K S S R N Q X X D C K X T V
T N X I O F J O I R A C I S R R W W X S K N Q I G
I N A C U O Y F I E M H C T A C M O V T M U Y L T
A I E I W K W J M C A H S L O D F U T O A N P A S
R D B P O H I E F J X I S Y O Z E X W I S T R I I
T E D S F W S D X O E T N N R N Y A V R S H O N L
X X C U T L B G I G J O N U S O E N S T J I E E E
P C L S L N X A E G Y I N Q L V T D F A S N L G N
U O M E W A A R K O E T B I H K V S Z P V K T N C
B M W V S W N M H B R Q L B J A N C I H P A S O E
L P G O A K K S R A T K S K Z E H Z Z B Q B U C O
I A V B G I N A C O I M F Q M B O C H D F L H S F
C N D A E R S E E N F I M A W I Y C C E Y E N S T
E Y U I X C A A G N C N R F C I A F C M A S A I H
N Y R G O B I D O R U K I F C E N R A Q R T C M E
E O O S L X O G H G F R O B R N O D B N V J I X L
M U A E W M A N J E M I L B G N O F R V L W R V A
I K N W Z R G U L I H L K C L Q T O F I D O E L M
E E E V D W K T Q C O R K Y R O M A N O V Y M R B
S E T D W O L F O F W A L L S T R E E T J E A P S
K P E D A W L K K A H A N N I B A L F O V T R N C
M R E T O O H S U R V E I L L A N C E Q U B T O W

#19

FBI ON TV

What most people know about the FBI comes from books, TV, and movies. Some films and fiction feature an accurate portrayal of the FBI, while others are not so successful.

Locate and redact or circle the following words within the grid. The words may be hidden horizontally, vertically, or diagonally and may appear backward or forward. Ignore words contained within parentheses.

(The) AMERICANS
(The) BLACKLIST
BLINDSPOT
BONES
CITY ON THE HILL
CRIMINAL MINDS
DECLASSIFIED
(The) ENEMY WITHIN
FBI
(The) F.B.I.
FBI FILES
(The) FRINGE
GONE
GRACELAND
HANNIBAL
LIMITLESS
(The) LOOMING TOWER
MANHUNT: UNABOMBER
MCMILLIONS
MINDHUNTER
NUMBERS
PERCEPTION
PROFILER
QUANTICO
TWIN PEAKS
UNSUB
WACO
WHISKEY CAVALIER
WHITE COLLAR
WITHOUT A TRACE
(The) X-FILES

#19

FBI ON TV

A W H M L A B I N N A H N E F Z Y R Y Z X H W M W

A H M A A R M D W C P F L V B X F S Y F Y I D O I

R I C K C N P R E T E H N G I I B F F S A N Q C T

E S U R Z B H Z O I O W F M I N D H U N T E R A H

W K M K I P R U V W F P R H T G S S A O P D L W O

O E K L U M V J N Z P I S X O R U A X I E T E W U

T Y K J S W I T V T L U S D V M X F I L E S N H T

G C A T A M H N N B U R N S N R N T A L L W E I A

N A B O N E S M A U R N D D A I B R J I L O M T T

I V M I S J I T K L Q Z A Q Z L L J I M I F Y E R

M A P K R G E T J J M N F B Q I C B V C H J W C A

O L Y D E I Q T T V T I Q F O N E E Y M E F I O C

O I I G B X R X W S T U N R O M H S D F H G T L E

L E W Y M I H A I B H R N D B M B S K L T N H L F

R R Z G U N R L N E A C G S S I Z E L C N L I A B

V H X R N H K B P T N W L R U K N L R Q O D N R I

F M W S P C X U E J S O A X N B D T W H Y C A N F

Z E X E A R O G A Z N U G K E I S I Q F T H V A I

B G W L W U O L K G A N I C U K J M N K I T Q W L

Y N B S M J B F S X C F S M O O C I S V C P R D E

V I L G F B T K I W I M L P K W T L P B U G P I S

Q R Z Y R B Z S Y L R F J Y U G R A C E L A N D S

K F P I K Q W Z C M E P N O I T P E C R E P L Q I

P U Z B Y O A I M W M R M P E B A M R D M U R M E

H R D J Q G D K M A A T O C I T N A U Q J X Y E K

#20 SERIAL MURDER

Serial murder is the killing of two or more people carried out by the same person (or persons) during separate events and times. The Bureau was authorized to investigate violent crimes against interstate travelers in 1994 and serial killings specifically in 1998. Serial killing are still local murders. The FBI may investigate only when requested to do so by an appropriate law enforcement agency.

Locate and redact or circle the following words within the grid. The words may be hidden horizontally, vertically, or diagonally and may appear backward or forward. Ignore words contained within parentheses.

ABNORMAL BEHAVIOR

BAU (Behavioral Analysis Unit)

BONDAGE

CANNIBALISM

CODIS (Combined DNA Index System)

COLD CASE

DEVIANT

DNA PROFILE

FETISHIST

GARROTE

GRATIFICATION

HIGHWAY INITIATIVE

MISSING PERSONS

MUTILATION

NCAVC (National Center for the Analysis of Violent Crime)

NECROPHILIA

PERSONALITY DISORDER

PSYCHOLOGY

PSYCHOPATHY

RAPE

RITUALISTIC

SADISTIC

SERIAL MURDER

SEXUAL ASSAULT

SEXUAL SADIST

SOCIOPATH

STALKER

THRILL KILLING

TORTURE

VICAP (Violent Criminal Apprehension Program)

VICTIMS

VIOLENT OFFENDERS

#20

SERIAL MURDER

V L W M I S S I N G P E R S O N S P Z R R A N S P

L N N L S A D I S T I C F Z X R B X V A E Q U Q T

Z S T A L K E R F E R U T R O T U C J B D Q C W S

T T C U W T L T C I B X X S E E I H I N R N V L I

T L R P F Q G V P O T W Y E B T R U K O O Q A J D

F M Y Z P X I S N C L V W N T V F C H R S B C A A

N O F M V C Z D F J T V R Y M J Y Q Z M I I N I S

Y U L C T R A C A N N I B A L I S M N A D O V L L

U X J I E G I W F Q T K T X C D T S Q L Y E Z I A

U F M E E W D E Y U L Y W U V N H G H B T V V H U

Y S W B Q R T A A C V E G K I T R Z I E I I C P X

Q A O V P I H L E V R S R W O L I N Y H L T Q O E

L W J Y S N I P K V P E A Q L U L E G A A A I R S

O U B H A S A M A C S R T Q E A L L O V N I W C Y

A U I X T R U V O V Y I I X N S K I L I O T N E I

Y S Y I Y M D D E C C A F I T S I F O O S I O N L

T F C U R E I D I U H L I P O A L O H R R N I I A

O V Z O V S J O R C O M C Y F L L R C S E I T W T

P T Q I B O A E L O P U A E F A I P Y W P Y A R W

J A A S S O G G Y L A R T T E U N A S S Q A L F E

O N C U G B Z Y T D T D I O N X G N P P J W I G N

T M F I A P R P T C H E O R D E C D D D J H T S Q

D F D U V G Z C I A Y R N R E S S F B Q O G U F V

U H T A P O I C O S O C L A R V N L J X M I M D X

R M W P N W M X Q E B W R G S U N A N H K H P B M

#21 SERIAL KILLERS

Serial killers have become celebrity monsters captivating the interest of true crime and horror fans. This public fascination began in the late 1880s, after a series of unsolved murders of sex workers occurred in the Whitechapel area of London. The murders were committed by a still unknown individual who named himself "Jack the Ripper" and sent letters to the police claiming to be the killer

Locate and redact or circle the following words within the grid. The words may be hidden horizontally, vertically, or diagonally and may appear backward or forward. Ignore words contained within parentheses.

AILEEN WUORNOS
BODIES
BOSTON STRANGLER
BTK
CHARLES NG
DAVID BERKOWITZ
DENNIS RADER
EDMUND KEMPER
GARY RAY BOWLES
GARY RIDGEWAY
GOLDEN STATE KILLER
GREEN RIVER KILLER
HERB BAUMEISTER
HOMICIDE
JACK THE RIPPER
JEFFREY DAHMER
JOHN WAYNE GACY
KILLER
MURDERER
NIGHT STALKER
POGO
RICHARD RAMIREZ
SAMUEL LITTLE
SERIAL KILLER
SON OF SAM
TED BUNDY
WAYNE WILLIAMS
WILLIAM BONIN
ZODIAC

#21

SERIAL KILLERS

K Y W S G C J H R E L G N A R T S N O T S O B W T
R E T S I E M U A B B R E H P L D Z S A B T T V Q
R Y O G K Z G F U T G I J A C K T H E R I P P E R
C O B Y Z I Z H X Q N X L U M Y K J Q G P U J A T
A I L G W E L M C Z N H I P X T A C L V F D U M T
U A V V K T B L E R E L L I K R E V I R N E E R G
N Q N T N I Y R E N A R B L A U Y M D J M M P P D
E Y G R D W Z N N R O R I G A I H P W U P A E B P
V J P A E K U T N I S S C M Z O H Q R J F S D P K
R G E M R D O P R I N E E G A I K C V U A F I D T
E E A D F Y A B S E G O R I N R O H W U F O C O W
R T M R M S R R E J L H B I D S D U Z Z H N I B A
E P R H Y U O I S D S T T M A O E R E K F O M T Y
D Z K H A R N N D I L G T S A L B L A T Q S O E N
R T Q J U D A D R G N N O I T I K B R H K M H D E
U L J W S Z Y Y K O E N J F L A L I W A C I L B W
M V U E J O Z E B E U W E A A L L L L R H I M U I
P W P I Z D U D R O M W A D K T E K I L L C R N L
F L S P Z I F E S F W P N Y I I R U E W E W T D L
O Y A O K A Y L J Q F L E E I U W C M R M R N Y I
W C K G B C P Z M K D E E R E Z C V Z A E H S R A
Z Q V O H R I O W R A C J S D L K P Q M S R I P M
Y H C W G D A V I D B E R K O W I T Z D U A I D S
M Y C A G E N Y A W N H O J F J P A C X L R F F T
V F G O L D E N S T A T E K I L L E R X Y K H S J

#22 WHITE COLLAR CRIME

White collar crimes are those committed in the course of a business transaction and are characterized by deceit, fraud, and concealment to deprive others of money or property. The FBI generally focuses on complex investigations--often with a nexus to organized crime activities--that are international, national, or regional in scope, and where the FBI can bring to bear unique expertise or capabilities that increase the likelihood of successful investigations.

Locate and redact or circle the following words within the grid. The words may be hidden horizontally, vertically, or diagonally and may appear backward or forward. Ignore words contained within parentheses.

AMERICAN GREED
BRIBERY
CHEAT
CORPORATE FRAUD
CORRUPTION
COUNTERFEIT
DECEPTION
DISHONESTY
ETHICS
EXTORTION
FAKE
FINCEN (Financial Analysis Center)
FRAUD
GREED
HEALTHCARE FRAUD
IMPOSTER
KICKBACKS
KLEPTOCRACY
MANIPULATE
MONEY LAUNDERING
POWER
PRETENDERS
SCAM
SECURITIES
SELF-DEALING
SMISHING
SPOOFING
TELEMARKETING FRAUD
WHITE COLLAR

#22

WHITE COLLAR CRIME

O C L M I V O P R E T E N D E R S K G Y A D U U E
O V G M N E X T O R T I O N J Z X U B N X J L Z E
T N T Q Q V B G Z B I V T H I I Q B F U A A M P R
O O F Q L V X E Y H T H P A A D N S T A M A L B D
K L E P T O C R A C Y P L S E W V D R S C I H T E
Z E D W E B L E Q K B X J O O H B S P S Y S C G G
Z C F N L P F S Y B A H I O E T C W C B O D Q N L
O R P B K D E C E P T I O N Z G X L O S F Y I A D
C O R R U P T I O N R R Q V Z Y L Z W C R H G Z U
W Z T W Q D U A R F E T A R O P R O C E S N D J A
R Q G N I R E D N U A L Y E N O M W B I V N U S R
H E A L T H C A R E F R A U D R D I M P S D P S F
J D B E L F A O E E L S P I C N R S Z N B U V K G
Y A P W R J M B V U I G E F U B V H J Q Q A T C N
T Y O K A S E I T I R U C E S K Y Y F F X R G A I
S M L H L S R E C E C O U N T E R F E I T F T B T
E R A M L U I A E K A F J Q X K Z J P L G F R K E
N M U B O Y C D R L B Q R D D O I W W M I P T C K
O N R Q C D A Y X F U M O Z V Q M A U N Y N R I R
H G K I E P N J V R X U I B O M U V C X O B J K A
S V D S T R G W Y N R V M R O N X E J V J I F B M
I G H H I E R A S P O O F I N G N K L L A M B U E
D O L T H W E G N I L A E D F L E S P S N N N J L
C S Z E W O E G G V E T A L U P I N A M D E R K E
M S N V B P D N D H L N N E U S I M P O S T E R T

#23 ECONOMIC CRIME

Economic crimes are crimes committed in the course of a business transaction and are characterized by deceit, fraud, and concealment to deprive others of money or property. The motivation behind these crimes is financial--to obtain or avoid losing money, property, or services or to secure a personal or business advantage.

Locate and redact or circle the following words within the grid. The words may be hidden horizontally, vertically, or diagonally and may appear backward or forward. Ignore words contained within parentheses.

ADVANCE FEE
AUDITOR
BANKRUPTCY
BERNIE MADOFF
CLAWBACK
CON MAN
CORPORATION
ECONOMIC CRIME
EMBEZZLEMENT
ENRON
FORECLOSURE
FORFEITURE
FORGERY
IDENTITY THEFT
INSIDER TRADING
IRS AGENT
MAIL FRAUD
MORTGAGE FRAUD
OFFSHORE BANKS
PHISHING
PONZI SCHEME
POSTAL INSPECTOR
PRICE FIXING
PROMISSORY
PUMP AND DUMP
PYRAMID
SEC (Securities and Exchange Commission)
SWINDLER
TRADE SECRETS
WIRE FRAUD

#23

ECONOMIC CRIME

W M X F A T Q S K N A B E R O H S F F O D T U T T
I B P O D P Z G N I X I F E C I R P X Y H B Q F A
R O Y R V U S I F Q L W W F S F W T E R Q S N E E
E M R G A Q I M N U T V C P V Q W K R O D R Z H M
F I A E N P Q S S S S E C F V W V C U S J A A T E
R W M R C L O L T N I R Y Z L X L A S S K R T Y H
A D I Y E G U S Z E E D Q P V V A B O I S N S T C
U X D G F B B C T L R L E E W D R W L M R G H I S
D L X I E K O A D A O C R R U R V A C O E Z P T I
R H I P E N M N N M L U E A T K W L E R G F H N Z
I O F A M D I X T K T I R S Q R R C R P Y Z I E N
R T A A U W S K L I R F N B E S A J O M P C S D O
S N N E S Y Z Q E E L U A S E D B D F G K I H I P
A E U C P B A F N I K M P S P R A C I K T K I R X
G M Z O X E R R A Z X P X T D E N R T N C X N H E
E E G N P O O M O Z C R I A C I C I T X G J G Y Z
N L J O F N G S J H P B U X E Y Y T E B M B D R M
T Z E M A M D T G F C D N K Q T I P O M B O F Z O
I Z F I U L N V J Z I I N C Y Z A W D R A X W V G
C E A C P V W Y I T P O W N G C O I H K O D Z H J
G B X C P K M R O T L P M U D D N A P M U P O M E
R M K R S L I R N O I T A R O P R O C P Y O O F N
T E L I L A W W K R P S I X N X V D A L K H P D F
C S V M V J D Z S M Z K U P V L P O Q G B W T W U
X V P E F O M E G Y Q D U A R F E G A G T R O M I

#24 PUBLIC CORRUPTION

Public corruption, the FBI's top criminal investigative priority, poses a fundamental threat to our national security and way of life. No other law enforcement agency has attained the kind of success the FBI has achieved in combating corruption. This success is due largely to the FBI's skills and capabilities in running complex undercover operations and advanced surveillance methods.

Locate and redact or circle the following words within the grid. The words may be hidden horizontally, vertically, or diagonally and may appear backward or forward. Ignore words contained within parentheses.

ABUSE OF POWER

ALLEGATIONS

BAG MAN

BID RIGGING

BRIBERY

CAMPAIGN FINANCE

COLLUSION

CONFLICT OF INTEREST

CONSPIRACY

CONTRACT EXTORTION

DIVERSION OF GOODS

ELECTION FRAUD

EMBEZZLEMENT

FOREIGN INTERFERENCE

FRAUD

GRAFT

GRATUITIES

ICU (International Corruption Unit)

ILLEGAL DONATIONS

IMPROPER RELATIONSHIPS

INSPECTOR GENERAL

INTEGRITY

INVESTIGATIVE PRIORITY

KICKBACKS

KLEPTOCRACY

MISCONDUCT

MISUSE OF FUNDS

MONEY LAUNDERING

PUBLIC OFFICIALS

PUBLIC TRUST

TAX DOLLARS

UNDERCOVER STINGS

VOTER FRAUD

#24

PUBLIC CORRUPTION

C U K F R A U D S G N I T S R E V O C R E D N U Z
S Q Z G A D I V E R S I O N O F G O O D S R O U V
L O Y P B V A X S E I T I U T A R G O L W Y I Q C
A D B Q U G X L J L Y E Z T I S M U J W R G T T L
I Y T E S S T H V Y B X P C N Y P U F E Y U R Y S
C T Y U E P S S N W F W Q O V P E C B C A R O B H
I I C S O I L M X X J T I N E U H I W N N U T I T
F R A N F H J O K T U T R F S V R Q B E B N X L N
F G R A P S X N W Z A X I L T B Q F T R I S E L E
O E I Y O N W E Y G W H N I I B U E B E D D T E M
C T P X W O O Y E Z C Z S C G L W L Z F R N C G E
I N S C E I R L N G A W P T A K L E F R I U A A L
L I N N R T L A A Z M T E O T R N C A E G F R L Z
B Y O A M A C U P P P N C F I D Y T R T G F T D Z
U V C M Q L B N I U A Y T I V U T I U N I O N O E
P G S G R E C D C B I E O N E A X O U I N E O N B
H J R A K R K E I L G N R T P R J N M N G S C A M
R Y A B I R W R N I N O G E R F K F G G A U Y T E
C W L J C E X I X C F I E R I R I R G I G S A I L
X X L R K P Q N Y T I S N E O E J A R E X I R O M
P G O Q B O C G S R N U E S R T G U A R E M L N A
X U D O A R X S S U A L R T I O W D F O E U T S F
G P X N C P G Y M S N L A L T V S W T F I C U S O
Z W A Y K M Q T H T C O L Z Y C A R C O T P E L K
E C T T S I M I I G E C M I S C O N D U C T X Z F

#25 FBI WORKING DOGS

Working dogs are specially trained to assist agents and protect people by identifying evidence and potential dangers. They see work as a game for which they receive an edible treat, a favorite ball, or a chew toy as a reward for playing.

Locate and redact or circle the following words within the grid. The words may be hidden horizontally, vertically, or diagonally and may appear backward or forward. Ignore words contained within parentheses.

ALERT
BLOODHOUNDS
BODIES
BOMB SNIFFING
CADAVER DOG
DRUG DETECTION
FUGITIVES
GERMAN SHEPHERDS
HANDLER
HEARING
HUMAN REMAINS
MISSING PERSONS
NARCOTICS DETECTION
NATURAL DISASTERS
OBEDIENCE TRAINING
OBSERVATION
ODOR
PARTNER
PRACTICE
RESCUE
RETRIEVERS
REWARD
SARS (Search and Rescue Dogs)
SCENT
SEARCH
SERVICE ANIMAL
SMELL
SPECIALLY TRAINED
THERAPY DOG
TRACKING
TRAINING
TREAT
WORKING DOGS

#25

FBI WORKING DOGS

```
A S J M M N J P E D W B I S H O F R A F R T I F V
U X Y D G A B I U D I X D A H O T R E A T I Q R V
A L F G D T N O P B O H N K P F G E S C A L O U W
P P O T R U G J M W I D T S L O H T N R I D B K K
Q I D R U R S H Z B L I S E W K V R O V O S E P W
F W S E G A E M C E S R S C A G T I S B J S D X U
W P A L D L V G R R A N S G E V W E R L S A I H C
V O S A E D I O E L A T I E L N N V E D S R E W A
R M P D T I T D P R W E U F A Q T E P J S S N D D
E X E R E S I Y G T M B S O F H H R G D J U C C A
S E C A C A G P R M U A Z U E I K S N R C H E H V
C C I W T S U A E C G I N O F F N U I X J A T D E
U I A E I T F R N G S N Q S L T O G S O L O R T R
E T L R O E A E T D L U I Q H H L R S Y W S A K D
L C L C N R Y H R J B B O K D E S O I W R X I H O
G A Y O K S W T A I G F S O C W P Y M C D V N I G
S R T C H O G A P R P S O D U A G H K S A T I Z W
I P R F E E O B B U P L Q N R O R E E V F F N S W
P A A P Q G A R N L B Q P Y O E Z T W R B T G X R
S E I D O B T R S G O D G N I K R O W Q D B T R K
D Y N A R C O T I C S D E T E C T I O N D S Z Y B
E Z E D E Z H S Z N N A Q K O B S E R V A T I O N
F R D B I S S C B H G S M E L L O Y F N G Y G D S
K L R O U P A U X U B Y D H U M A N R E M A I N S
T A Q O A L A M I N A E C I V R E S J U G L W X T
```

#26 HOSTAGE RESCUE TEAM

The Hostage Rescue Team (HRT) is a tier-one tactical unit capable of responding to major critical incidents throughout the United States and the world.

Locate and redact or circle the following words within the grid. The words may be hidden horizontally, vertically, or diagonally and may appear backward or forward. Ignore words contained within parentheses.

ARMY RANGERS
ASSAULTER
BATTERING RAM
BREACHER
COUNTERTERRORISM
CRISIS SITE
DYNAMIC ASSAULT
ELITE TACTICAL UNIT
FAST ROPING
FIELD SWAT TEAMS
GAS MASK
GOGGLES
HALLIGAN TOOL
HELMET
HIGH-RISK RAIDS
HRT
JSOC (Joint Special Operations Command)
LIVE-FIRE TRAINING
MAJOR EVENTS
MISSION FOCUSED
NATIONAL SECURITY
NAVY SEALS
OLYMPIC GAMES
OPERATOR
PARAMILITARY
PHASE LINE GREEN
SHOOTING HOUSE
SLEDGEHAMMER
SNIPER
SPECIAL FORCES
SUBLOAD
TACTICAL TRAINING
TEAR GAS
TIER ONE

#26

HOSTAGE RESCUE TEAM

U T Q E B G T T L U A S S A C I M A N Y D M M U C

Q E A H S D S M A E T T A W S D L E I F C F C L C

Q M E I G N I N I A R T L A C I T C A T D L M I H

Y L A G T R M T E N Z B B P M S H M T S S L W V H

H E I H U E W S F W R K Z F G N E J E X C F Z E Z

T H P R O P R Y D E R U S J J Y S L G D E Z E F H

E B H I W I U O A T V A R M Y R A N G E R S C I A

G D D S P N Q C M S M D R S R V T A K G D A P R L

A H N K H S H F R E M M A H E G D E L S O Z X E L

S Y B R Y E S W U Y R A T I L I M A R A P G A T I

M M X A R D A O R C S S E M A G C I P M Y L O R G

A I S I Y T I R U C E S L A N O I T A N X F G A A

S S P D C E T I S S I S I R C D A O L B U S M I N

K S E S M S I R O R R E T R E T N U O C M H J N T

K I C A W M A R G N I R E T T A B T T Y L H V I O

Y O I D P H A S E L I N E G R E E N R J S K U N O

U N A O E N O R E I T H A X R T R S S M T B I G L

S F L P B H E S N Q P S R X V D A O S C M W F Q N

L O F E Z M L M V P S U O R S O C C R A L G K Z Q

F C O R Q B D T W A Y F A S T R O P I N G D W P H

U U R A M V F P U M A J O R E V E N T S T R I G P

V S C T I D T L B X Z I T L P V B W P L X R A J W

S E E O O N T R S S L A E S Y V A N E H W F H E S

X D S R B E C A U E E S U O H G N I T O O H S H T

B X A F R U N F T I N U L A C I T C A T E T I L E

#27 INTERNATIONAL TERRORISM

International terrorism is violent, criminal acts committed by individuals and/or groups who are inspired by, or associated with, foreign terrorist organizations or nations. Protecting the United States from terrorist attacks is the FBI's number one priority. The Bureau works closely with its partners to neutralize terrorist cells and operatives here in the United States, to help dismantle extremist networks worldwide, and to cut off financing and other forms of support provided to foreign terrorist organizations.

Locate and redact or circle the following words within the grid. The words may be hidden horizontally, vertically, or diagonally and may appear backward or forward. Ignore words contained within parentheses.

- AL QAEDA
- BIN LADEN
- CHATTER
- DETAINEES
- EMBASSY BOMBING
- EMBEDDED
- EXTRATERRITORIAL
- EXTREMISTS
- HIJACKERS
- HOMELAND SECURITY
- ISIS (Islamic State of Iraq and Syria)
- JTTF (Joint Terrorism Task Force)
- KIDNAPPING
- MATERIAL SUPPORT
- NAME CHECK
- NEUTRALIZE
- OPERATIVES
- OVERSEAS
- PENTAGON ATTACK
- RADICALIZE
- SAFE HOUSES
- SCREENING CENTER
- SHANKSVILLE
- SHOE BOMBER
- SLEEPER CELL
- SUICIDE BOMBER
- TEDAC (Terrorist Explosive Device Analytical Center)
- TERRORIST CELLS
- TERRORIST FINANCING
- TRAINING CAMPS
- TWIN TOWERS
- USS COLE
- WAR ZONE
- WATCH LIST
- WMD (Weapons of Mass Destruction)
- WORLD TRADE CENTER

#27 INTERNATIONAL TERRORISM

F O O E M G N I C N A N I F T S I R O R R E T O B

Z T V H I S R Z Q G T D E T A I N E E S P G O X T

H N F A K C A T T A N O G A T N E P F T Z P R H N

A E M H H O M E L A N D S E C U R I T Y T V P I K

F U A K C E H C E M A N E Q G I K W M H I A B M X

R T T E S M R E B M O B E O H S V H U S G Y H L I

B R E J C C N L L E C R E P E E L S U T H R L C W

K A R I R S L L E C T S I R O R R E T S V A N L E

P L I R E T N E C E D A R T D L R O W I H D O J X

D I A L E T W T W Y E M B A S S Y B O M B I N G T

M Z L D N U Q I I N A M O V B M U V O E X C G T R

W E S W I C E I N W M L R E B E T X N R S A T S A

L V U F N T S S L T C E Q D G H X L G T A L T I T

S Z P I G R O I E F O A L A G J S Q N X E I A L E

H J P H C A M S I S T W D O E O W K I E S Z G H R

A Y O S E I T M P Q U T E E C D Y U P K R E F C R

N G R R N N B J L R Z O J R T S A Z P R E L X T I

K E T E T I E C X R L D H W S E S L A Y V N Q A T

S V E K E N B D W H N K V E C A N U N E O A C W O

V R N C R G G P A S H M R D F Z D E D D E B M E R

I F O A D C B B B L M U U I L A S Q I F H O J L I

L P Z J V A I W R Y N W P T W G S L K D L V N W A

L W R I S M G M I J I I G E O P E R A T I V E S L

E S A H I P M L Y B I V B X W U C O F E M H P N I

F A W W C S I L R E B M O B E D I C I U S V D Z G

#28 DOMESTIC TERRORISM

Domestic terrorism is violent, criminal acts committed by individuals and/or groups to further ideological goals stemming from domestic influences, such as those of a political, religious, social, racial, or environmental nature. The acts may also promote anti-government sentiment and must occur primarily within the jurisdiction of the United States. Frequently, those involved in domestic terrorism have no clear group affiliation or guidance, making them challenging to identify, investigate, and disrupt.

Locate and redact or circle the following words within the grid. The words may be hidden horizontally, vertically, or diagonally and may appear backward or forward. Ignore words contained within parentheses.

ACTIVE SHOOTER
ALF (Animal Liberation Front)
ANTHRAX
ANTI-ABORTION VIOLENCE
ARYAN NATIONS
BLACK LIBERATION ARMY
BOMB THREAT
CIVIL DISORDER
COUNTERTERRORISM
DEMONSTRATION
ECO-TERRORISTS
FEAR
HATE
HOMEGROWN
IDEOLOGY
INTIMIDATION
JEWISH DEFENSE LEAGUE
KU KLUX KLAN
LONE WOLF
MASS SHOOTINGS
ORGANIZED ENTERPRISES
PATRIOT ACT
POSSE COMITATUS
SOVEREIGN CITIZENS
TED KACZYNSKI
TERRY NICHOLS
THE ORDER
THREAT
TIMOTHY MCVEIGH
UNABOMBER
VIOLENCE
WEATHER UNDERGROUND
WHITE SUPREMACISTS

#28 DOMESTIC TERRORISM

S F K Q A Z F W H I T E S U P R E M A C I S T S U

V O U W U T L D E W A G Y C M Y G B N X I T L P N

I U K U W H O D D L P A E A U M M X T P I S Q F A

O B L J X E W U N T H O U A C R M X I P L G S K B

L Y U G G O E Q U E W G G C L A K F A R D E E C O

E O X I I R N U O D T P A S V N V Z B E W R S I M

N H K F T D O B R K T R E N O O Z O O D T C I K B

C O L O R E L O G A J A L E R I W K R R T O R D E

E M A Q Y R S M R C Q R E Z C T M M T O I U P P R

U E N D C W V B E Z K Y S I O A Y K I S M N R O P

H G O R M I T T D Y W A N T F R P S O I O T E S D

K R I R R A Q H N N Z N E I C E W L N D T E T S E

S O T E F S E R U S B N F C D B F O V L H R N E M

T W A T A F T E R K H A E N Z I E H I I Y T E C O

S N D O N L D A E I T T D G I L A C O V M E D O N

I V I O P G T T H K F I H I Y K R I L I C R E M S

R U M H X A R H T N A O S E W C C N E C V R Z I T

O T I S M B R U A H M N I R D A E Y N A E O I T R

R H T E Z Q S J E A X S W E G L O R C C I R N A A

R R N V X F J G W T K C E V V B B R E V G I A T T

E E I I K J F S R E H X J O H Z Q E Z N H S G U I

T A Z T U V I L F D D Q L S S Z F T H H S M R S O

O T L C Q R K G Q L Y B T C A T O I R T A P O T N

C Z H A H I U C Y Q A P O Y G O L O E D I Y K N Y

E Z Y S L J S K A K S G N I T O O H S S S A M K O

#29 CRISIS INCIDENT RESPONSE

The FBI successfully resolves critical incidents worldwide by rapidly responding to events with "one-stop-shop" expertise. The Critical Incident Response Group (CIRG) was established in 1994 to integrate tactical, negotiation, behavioral analysis, and crisis management resources into one cohesive structure. CIRG personnel also assist FBI field divisions and law enforcement partners with pre-crisis planning for special events.

Locate and redact or circle the following words within the grid. The words may be hidden horizontally, vertically, or diagonally and may appear backward or forward. Ignore words contained within parentheses.

ACTIVE SHOOTER

ASSESSMENTS

AVIATION SUPPORT

BARRICADE

BEHAVIORAL ANALYSIS

BOMB

BOMB DOGS

CIRG

ENHANCED SWAT

FLY TEAM

HOSTAGE RESCUE TEAM

HRFC (Hostage Recovery Fusion Cell)

INAUGURATION

INCIDENT COMMANDER

INFORMATION SHARING

INTERMEDIARIES

INTERNATIONAL

KIDNAPPINGS

LOGISTICS

MASS SHOOTING

NATURAL DISASTER

NEGOTIATOR

OLYMPICS

OVERSEAS DEPLOYMENT

PRISON RIOTS

RAPID DEPLOYMENT

READINESS

RESOLUTION

ROADBLOCKS

SIOC (Strategic Information Operations Center)

SUPER BOWL

TRACKING DOGS

WHEELS UP

WORKPLACE VIOLENCE

#29 CRISIS INCIDENT RESPONSE

T I N F O R M A T I O N S H A R I N G K S I W P F
N N S X L M J W Y B N D H F P M G N I S H S R C B
Z F T N T Z N U B B M A E T Y L F D E Q P E T T A
X C U O N T O D A D T V H M B M N N J F D B N R N
P F N S E M I U R O W C M O N A I S E N L O E O O
Y N O I M U T I R M M F E L P D T B A M W M M P I
S C K S Y N U O I W V P X P A N N M S A O B Y P T
J H K Y O A L P C O D U I E E E M L B S B D O U A
A I Z L L T O G A Z F N R M G O G G M S R O L S R
D P Z A P U S D D B G E S O C D U K K S E G P N U
A Z S N E R E H E S W S T T R U U Q C H P S E O G
I C C A D A R Z F F E I N R A E E C I O U B D I U
N M I L D L D F H S A E Q I L H T G R O S G S T A
T S P A I D G L S T D T S K L C T L G T H L A A N
E G M R P I F A O I P D H G Y Y Y Z X I B C E I I
R O Y O A S I R C H S C I T S I G O L N F S S V J
N D L I R A Y N K R O A D B L O C K S G K A R A O
A G O V J S I W H O S T A G E R E S C U E T E A M
T N N A M T A C T I V E S H O O T E R M G P V C L
I I R H T E A Y I N T E R M E D I A R I E S O P E
O K I E B R N J T A W S D E C N A H N E U H J E J
N C C B P U S L E E H W K L F S S U B B C O I S X
A A F L R F H U U M R J X L K I I I P M O A W X A
L R R F G A R D B P R I S O N R I O T S O A B X J
Q T H E C N E L O I V E C A L P K R O W Q B W O H

#30 SIOC AND COMMAND CENTERS

The Strategic Information and Operations Center (SIOC) is the FBI's global command and communications center. It operates around the clock to maintain enterprise-wide situational awareness and to provide FBI leadership with strategic information by serving as a clearinghouse to collect, process, and disseminate information in a timely manner. SIOC leverages existing resources and provides a platform for more informed decision-making.

Locate and redact or circle the following words within the grid. The words may be hidden horizontally, vertically, or diagonally and may appear backward or forward. Ignore words contained within parentheses.

COMMAND POST

COMPUTER TERMINALS

COP (Common Operation Picture)

DECISION-MAKING

ELECTRONIC LIBRARIES

EXECUTIVE BRIEFINGS

FUSION CELLS

HIGH-TECH

INFORMATION PROCESSING

JIC (Joint Information Center)

JOC (Joint Operations Center)

MAJOR CASE

MISSION-ORIENTED

MOBILE COMMAND

NATIONAL EMERGENCIES

OPERATIONAL OVERSIGHT

REAL-TIME MONITORING

SATELLITE RADIOS

SCIF (Sensitive Compartmented Information Facility)

SECURE TELEPHONES

SIOC

STATE OF READINESS

STATE-OF-THE-ART

TELECOMMUNICATIONS CENTER

TELECONFERENCING

TIME-SENSITIVE

VIDEO WALL

VIRTUAL COMMAND CENTER

WATCH CENTER

#30 SIOC AND COMMAND CENTERS

C T J I C T L L Z R O K Y E B N S C P R Z L W E T
G M G M V I R T U A L C O M M A N D C E N T E R E
S V N O Z H F A S K Z G E Z C D O I I M V H W O L
E J I B V W Z A B P M N L G S O E U F W C E H P E
C Y S I M D E U J R V A E N Y Y B K O E N V G E C
U I S L M P X Z U O K Q C I W Y G Q T N O I F R O
R M E E C R E R T K C S T C B F W H S A H T H A M
E A C C O K C E R W I A R N B F G O L T S I V T M
T J O O M X U A A A Y T O E Q I A Y A I S S G I U
E O R M M K T L E B P E N R H W U L N O E N D O N
L R P M A L I T H Q C L I E N A X D I N N E E N I
E C N A N G V I T C P L C F L T I O M A I S T A C
P A O N D N E M F X W I L N L C O H R L D E N L A
H S I D P I B E O G W T I O A H M E E E A M E O T
O E T N O K R M E U F E B C W C P T T M E I I V I
N V A A S A I O T P P R R E O E Q Y R E R T R E O
E H M I T M E N A M L A A L E N S K E R F V O R N
S Q R I I N F I T L Y D R E D T C C T G O Y N S S
M I O D C O I T S C T I I T I E I R U E E K O I C
X X F B A I N O F W X O E G V R F N P N T H I G E
N M N R B S G R F K L S S D M P C N M C A D S H N
T P I R H I S I D K S Y M W Y O N J O I T L S T T
L K E Y T C B N V P D K P H I K D S C E S R I Z E
H B W T E E L G O I Y T M S O P V R O S D R M U R
Z A Y N W D L C I P F B S L L E C N O I S U F Z S

#31 SPECIAL AGENT BOMB TECH

Special Agent Bomb Techs (SABT) coordinate liaison and training with their local police and military counterparts. They routinely respond to calls about suspicious packages or bomb threats and are on standby to support local police departments at major events. After a bomb has exploded, a SABT will monitor the processing and evidence collection at the post-blast crime scene and may be asked to testify in court as an expert witness.

Locate and redact or circle the following words within the grid. The words may be hidden horizontally, vertically, or diagonally and may appear backward or forward. Ignore words contained within parentheses.

ATF (Bureau of Alcohol, Tobacco, Firearms and Explosives)

BLASTING CAPS

BOMB TECH

BOMB THREATS

CONTAMINATION

COORDINATION

CRIME SCENE

DESTRUCTION

DETONATE

DEVICES

DISMANTLE

EMERGENCY RESPONDERS

EQUIPMENT

EVACUATE

EVIDENCE RESPONSE

EXPLOSIVES EXPERT

HAND ENTRY

IED (Improvised Explosive Device)

INCENDIARY DEVICE

LABORATORY

MAJOR EVENTS

POST BLAST

PROTECTIVE COVERINGS

REDSTONE ARSENAL

REMOTE EQUIPMENT

RENDER SAFE

RESIDUE

SABT

SAFE ZONES

SPECIALIZED TRAINING

SUSPICIOUS PACKAGES

TEDAC (Terrorist Explosive Device Analytical Center)

TYVEK SUITS

#31 SPECIAL AGENT BOMB TECH

F S R I Z E K V Q V D P O S T B L A S T U F L P K
S T E Z Y N M T U L W Y R T N E D N A H K D E G T
S P N G S A F E Z O N E S B D E V I C E S R R T L
Z G A E A D M L H Y D T Y V E K S U I T S E S Z K
P C N C M K E N E C S   E M I R C C E T E V P X P
A K O I G P C E F V S J T V Y E A A W Z D I E C O
E M A O R N I A L T M L Y O R T D P T I U D C J E
T W T F R E I U P T J A J D B A E G M F Y E I B C
S R Q J Q D V T Q S N M L Y A U T W W L P N A O I
E A E S L R I O S E U A L T P C M Y A X B C L M V
L T M P Z U Z N C A E O M N X A A C A W C E I B E
A H B F X R I X A E L T I S M V K D B C J R Z T D
N I E Y L E P M W T V B O C I E D M U O P E E H Y
E L F N P T S Y M Z I I G M I D X E J N Y S D R R
S N A P O C Z E H A V O T J E P K J I T R P T E A
R N S Y D I B N V C J M N C X R S S C A O O R A I
A R R V N X T K D I E O P G E G Q U R M T N A T D
E I E H R C A C D W S T R O Y T K M S I A S I S N
N E D O B G Z Y U I T O B E C Z O R B N R E N W E
O U N I K K L D M R M T L M V P S R S A O B I G C
T D E G B B J P J T T S E P O E G M P T B R N L N
S I R F H T B A S N D S R Z X B N G L I A J G S I
D S P D E T O N A T E S E T C E M T Q O L W W I E
E E S R T N E M P I U Q E D G R T J S N I I D D D
R R Y U S G S R E D N O P S E R Y C N E G R E M E

#32 WEAPONS OF MASS DESTRUCTION

Each FBI field office has a weapons of mass destruction (WMD) coordinator whose primary function is to coordinate the assessment of and response to incidents involving the use or threatened use of chemical, biological, and radiological/nuclear materials. Each WMD coordinator is tasked with establishing appropriate liaison with regional, state, and local emergency response personnel as well as with critical facilities within each field office's jurisdiction in order to facilitate notification and response to WMD incidents.

Locate and redact or circle the following words within the grid. The words may be hidden horizontally, vertically, or diagonally and may appear backward or forward. Ignore words contained within parentheses.

ANTHRAX
ATTACKS
BIOLOGICAL AGENT
BIOSECURITY
BIOTERRORISM
BOTULISM
CDC (Center for Disease Control and Prevention)
CHEMICAL THREAT
CONTAGIOUS
CONTAMINATION
COORDINATOR
COUNTERMEASURES
CRITICAL INFRASTRUCTURE
DESTRUCTIVE DEVICE
DIAGNOSIS
EPIDEMIOLOGY
EXPOSURE
FIELD TESTING
INCIDENT RESPONSE
INFRAGARD
INTELLIGENCE-DRIVEN
LARGE SCALE
MODE OF TRANSMISSION
NATIONAL SECURITY
NUCLEAR MATERIALS
NUCLEAR PROLIFERATION
OUTBREAKS
PREPAREDNESS
PRIVATE SECTOR
PUBLIC HEALTH
QUARANTINE
RADIOLOGICAL
SARS
SUSPICIOUS PURCHASES
THREAT ASSESSMENT
VACCINES
WHITE POWDER
WMD

#32 WEAPONS OF MASS DESTRUCTION

J S Y C J G N N X P N W E P I D E M I O L O G Y M
S O R M Y F Y T I R U C E S O I B W U F Q Z G R S
Z F M S L H A H Q L W F S U O I G A T N O C V C I
S C I N T E L L I G E N C E D R I V E N Z F U R R
U M D Z W C E L A C S E G R A L L K H R Z A E I O
B H N C S T S L J R A D I O L O G I C A L A N T R
B V U N O I S S I M S N A R T F O E D O M M I I R
H N C O B D C O N T A M I N A T I O N V H C T C E
E C L N U C L E A R P R O L I F E R A T I O N A T
C H E S E S A H C R U P S U O I C I P S U S A L O
I E A Y T I R U C E S L A N O I T A N D N W R I I
V M R O L S E R U S A E M R E T N U O C M W A N B
E I M N I N C I D E N T R E S P O N S E G W U F U
D C A X U T N E G A L A C I G O L O I B B K Q R U
E A T I Z G I T D N J I S K A E R B T U O Y E A Z
V L E H E M I D R A G A R F N I A N T H R A X S A
I T R H P A W H I T E P O W D E R O M L D M S T S
T H I W W F L R M G A K S Y O I T A S K S E A R E
C R A R O T C E S E T A V I R P T T I S E X R U N
U E L Y K R O T A N I D R O O C M T L O I P S C I
R A S U M X N M S I S O N G A I D A U K F O X T C
T T N E M S S E S S A T A E R H T C T V T S M U C
S P R E P A R E D N E S S W X C S K O W S U D R A
E O H T L A E H C I L B U P P G Y S B Z H R X E V
D X G W G F G N I T S E T D L E I F C K I E X R F

#33 FBI LABORATORY

The FBI laboratory provides forensic examinations, technical support, expert witness testimony, and training to federal, state, and local law enforcement agencies, as well as operational response to events, such as terrorist attacks and natural disasters, all around the world. Forensic examiners are highly educated scientists and expertly trained technicians; each with their own specialty. The FBI Laboratory can be used by authorized police departments and provides examinations and testimony in state court at no cost to the summoning law enforcement agencies.

Locate and redact or circle the following words within the grid. The words may be hidden horizontally, vertically, or diagonally and may appear backward or forward. Ignore words contained within parentheses.

ANALYSIS
BALLISTIC TESTING
BIOMETRIC ANALYSIS
BITE MARKS
BLOOD SPATTER
BODILY FLUIDS
CHAIN OF CUSTODY
CHEMISTRY UNIT
CODIS (Combined DNA Index System)
"CSI" EFFECT
DNA TESTING
EVIDENCE RESPONSE TEAM
EVIDENTIARY EXAM
EXCAVATE
EXEMPLARS
EXPERT WITNESS
FORENSIC PHOTOGRAPHY
FORENSICS LAB
FSRTC (Forensic Science Research and Training Center)
HAIR AND FIBERS
LATENT PRINTS
MITOCHONDRIAL DNA
QUESTIONED DOCUMENTS
SCIENTISTS
SEMEN
TESTIMONY
TOOL MARKS
TRACE EVIDENCE

#33

FBI LABORATORY

J T R A C E E V I D E N C E J N I B Y T S G O D Y
S Z O C L P L O Y P A C B I L G P F S H N U E Q R
K S T N R E T T A P S D O O L B W V X G U Z B S Q
R I D N A T E S T I N G R R S I S Y L A N A J K R
A S S D K J H C S I E F F E C T M Z Q S E M N G Q
M Y F O R E N S I C S L A B D V E X G K S B P T A
L L I F D Z P V P X V I P U Q T V H N K G A N F F
O A D S U G S L C P U T G R I C I Z I C B N D O E
O N C M K V D G O R F T R W N B D Q T A L D N R J
T A Q H H O Y K D O A E A B W R E S S D S L Z E S
M C N T A V N R I D G S U I D K N R E Z S A M N T
A I C B I I N A S P C T S T C G C E T F E I S S N
X R S G V N N E S J V I M E E T E B C S N R C I I
E T R Y K U U O M G O M N M F E R I I R T D I C R
Y E A A Z K M Y F E T O R A K Y E F T T I N E P P
R M L Q E V L X R C S N K R Z Y S D S C W O N H T
A O P H T T L X E T U Y U K M S P N I E T H T O N
I I M Y N V A S P T S S X S P V O A L W R C I T E
T B E O C I P V M P K I T T T A N R L B E O S O T
N H X J Y M N N A D P B M O J O S I A G P T T G A
E F E O G V R I W C X W C E D N E A B L X I S R L
D V Y E Z I T A T S X D R E H Y T H W G E M C A G
I U Z T M Z V D B F T E T K W C E C E F V N Q P P
V I D H B O D I L Y F L U I D S A I J V O B W H C
E Y Q U E S T I O N E D D O C U M E N T S L G Y Q

#34 EVIDENCE RESPONSE TEAM - 1

In most instances, being on an Evidence Response Team (ERT) is a collateral or ancillary assignment, and ERT members are responsible for performing their regular investigative and administrative duties. However, when activated, ERT members use their highly specialized training to document and collect forensic evidence from crime scenes, searches, and crisis situations in such a manner that the evidence may be introduced in courts throughout the United States and the world.

Locate and redact or circle the following words within the grid. The words may be hidden horizontally, vertically, or diagonally and may appear backward or forward. Ignore words contained within parentheses.

ADHESIVE TAPE
BODY FARM
BOMB DEBRIS
BOOTIES
BULLET TRAJECTORIES
CAMERAS
CASE NUMBER
CHAIN OF CUSTODY
COLLATERAL DUTY
COLLECT
COMPUTER SYSTEMS

CRIME SCENE TAPE
CROSS CONTAMINATION
DECONTAMINATE
DIVE TEAM
DNA
DOCUMENTATION
DUMP SITE
ERT
EVIDENCE COLLECTION
EVIDENCE MARKERS
FBI LABORATORY

FINGERPRINTS
FLASHLIGHT
FOOTPRINT MOLD
FORENSIC RESPONSE
GRID SEARCH
HAZARDOUS RESPONSE
HAZMAT HUMAN REMAINS
INFRARED
LATEX GLOVES
LIGHT SOURCE

#34 EVIDENCE RESPONSE TEAM – 1

T O Q N O C A S E N U M B E R Q O S M T V N P B K
Y E D L O M T N I R P T O O F W U J A S I O E O D
V Q L I G H T S O U R C E E E R E Q U B E R I E O S
Q H A Z A R D O U S R E S P O N S E B I X T P T F
F T F P B Q M N I F L A S H L I G H T R C C A I J
W P J B A H I C S B O M B D E B R I S O O E T E T
Y P S Z I X O M N S X Y K C D Z F J A T L L E S C
Z Q A E K L H O I M Q H I V V P I H S C L L N E R
A J K W L D I M A E F L H D D R N B N E A O E S O
L E J E M P J L M T A C X M J Y G L O J T C C N S
R N C A C A D H E S I V E T A P E E I A E E S O S
F T W Q N G K S R Y T D G R N K R T T R R C E P C
B G D L O D W M N S H D W D O W P A A T A N M S O
I R E A D M I A A R A X G U A G R N T T L E I E N
L I R T M K T E M E J A O M Y F I I N E D D R R T
A D A E H N L T U T R S L P G G N M E L U I C C A
B S R X X W A E H U L G Q S I M T A M L T V J I M
O E F G P O A V T P T V S I Z J S T U U Y E L S I
R A N L G T M I A M I M W T Q R A N C B P L X N N
A R I O D R G D M O C D B E G O A O O W B G Z E A
T C L V A X L E Z C L U L H H F M C D T P J E R T
O H V E P Q R S A B S A R E M A C E M L W U R O I
R S R S T T V L H B O D Y F A R M D J R G I A F O
Y W T F O V A P W M Y D O T S U C F O N I A H C N
T E V I D E N C E M A R K E R S J O R B T L G I F

#35 EVIDENCE RESPONSE TEAM - 2

In most instances, being on an Evidence Response Team (ERT) is a collateral or ancillary assignment, and ERT members are responsible for performing their regular investigative and administrative duties. However, when activated, ERT members use their highly specialized training to document and collect forensic evidence from crime scenes, searches, and crisis situations in such a manner that the evidence may be introduced in courts throughout the United States and the world.

Locate and redact or circle the following words within the grid. The words may be hidden horizontally, vertically, or diagonally and may appear backward or forward. Ignore words contained within parentheses.

MAGNETIC POWDER
MASKS
MASS GRAVES
MEASURING TOOLS
NATURAL DISASTERS
OPERATIONS LOG
PALM PRINT
PHOTO LOG
PHOTOGRAPH
PLANE CRASHES
PRESERVATION
PROCESS
RAPID DEPLOYMENT
RECOVERY
REMOTE SITE
RESPIRATORS
SCANNERS
SHOOTING INCIDENTS
SITE SKETCH
STAINS
SUBJECT-MATTER EXPERTS
SWAB
TAMPER-PROOF
TARPS
TEAM LEADER
TEAMWORK
TERRORISM ACTS
TIMELINE
TOOLS AND EQUIPMENT
TYVEK SUITS
UNDERWATER SEARCH
VICTIM RECOVERY
VIDEO
WORLD EVENTS

#35 EVIDENCE RESPONSE TEAM – 2

U T P V I R S H O O T I N G I N C I D E N T S Q O

L J J L A M Q P D J G P R T Y S Q N W B F Q G S G

P C F G O I W B J Y H O N O O T K N Z F X D F V A

F A K I M R W C A O C Y G L Z A I S T D G G U Y H

O T L U L R D F T W J D N R E R B K A K S V R T T

O O R M G T K O R C S N F V J P T Z C M F Y E C F

R Z R I P M G M Y P G C J P X S V I D E O A M H M

P M G G B R Z K T O R E C O V E R Y Q Z O T O T S

R S C W A L I I N W C S R E N N A C S K B E T H E

E T E P N P T N X I U B G O L S N O I T A R E P O

P C H W A V I C T I M R E C O V E R Y G M V S K Z

M A S O T R E S P I R A T O R S X C V F C S I R N

A M E R U Y F V O A R E D A E L M A E T N D T O O

T S V L R N H C R A E S R E T A W R E D N U E W L

K I A D A C F P R O C E S S T I U S K E V Y T M P

B R R E L U M E A S U R I N G T O O L S V F E A H

V O G V D S R T S N S E H S A R C E N A L P F E O

G R S E I W T N E M P I U Q E D N A S L O O T T T

O R S N S G R Q Z R O S N I A T S F C J P P F U O

U E A T A G Q W J Q X D G E N I L E M I T P B H

Z T M S S V E N I I R E D W O P C I T E N G A M L

T Q O H T V V H C T E K S E T I S K L Q V S L Q O

S U B J E C T M A T T E R E X P E R T S P P Y X G

N B Q W R P N O I T A V R E S E R P Z L Z C O S R

S B P B S G V O R A P I D D E P L O Y M E N T F M

#36 MAJOR CASES

The following are some of the major cases featuring the top priorities investigated by the FBI.

Locate and redact or circle the following words within the grid. The words may be hidden horizontally, vertically, or diagonally and may appear backward or forward. Ignore words contained within parentheses.

ABSCAM

ALDRICH AMES

AMERITHRAX

ATLANTA CHILD MURDERS

BELTWAY SNIPERS

BOSTON MARATHON

EMBASSY BOMBINGS

ENRON

ERIC RUDOLPH

JFK ASSASSINATION

JOHN HINCKLEY JR.

JONESTOWN

LINDBERGH KIDNAPPING

MAJOR CASES

MIAMI SHOOTOUT

MILBURN (Mississippi Burning)

OKLAHOMA CITY BOMBING

OPERATION GOLDENROD

OPERATION GREYLORD

PAN AM BOMBING

PATTY HEARST

PENTTBOM (9/11 Attacks)

RESMURS (Reservation Murders)

ROBERT HANSSEN

RUBY RIDGE

UNABOMBER

USS COLE BOMBING

WACO

WATERGATE

WEATHER UNDERGROUND

WORLD TRADE CENTER

#36

MAJOR CASES

K C E B A U R I S X E A U C P D C F E P T R D D F
A K G W V T R J B E B F L W P X U F P S U E O C N
X F D E G R L H Y S S L J Q K I T Z N W O T R G E
D E I A N V Y A C E P A D S R A Y J X N T N N B S
Q R R T I X T A N A L J C P N W A E Z R O E E O S
G I Y H P N M I G T S K W R J A M X B U O C D S N
N C B E P S O Q N L A C C W O P L A L B H E L T A
I R U R A U X A I H H C J N K J U L X L S D O O H
B U R U N N J M B Z S B H O I E A L Q I I A G N T
M D V N D A B E M D R H E I N H P M X M M R N M R
O O H D I B W R O I U Q N L L E N A I E A T O A E
B L B E K O A I B H M H X P T D S H M Z I D I R B
M P C R H M T T E W S P H S A W M T O F M L T A O
A H Y G G B E H L X E L M Q N T A U O J T R A T R
N P B R R E R R O T R O I U H R T Y R W D O R H R
A U J O E R G A C G Z F T D P L M Y S D N W E O E
P J T U B F A X S U P E N T T B O M H N E K P N C
R A V N D W T A S Z G O S N C I S Z D E I R O F H
Y E V D N X E M U F S C E I O W E B P G A P S H N
A L D R I C H A M E S A U X S R P R I V T R E J Z
H C L K L Q I G W K P W K W Y W N Y V N Z V S R Y
O P E R A T I O N G R E Y L O R D E R L U U Y T S
C L P P Q I G N I B M O B Y T I C A M O H A L K O
C O S G N I B M O B Y S S A B M E M Y Q T X G W U
S W S N O I T A N I S S A S S A K F J D Y Y V R W

#37

ART THEFT

Art and cultural property crime—which includes theft, fraud, looting, and trafficking across state and international lines—is a looming criminal enterprise with estimated losses in the billions of dollars annually. The agents assigned to the FBI rapid deployment Art Crime Team are responsible for addressing art and cultural property crime cases in assigned geographic regions and around the world.

Locate and redact or circle the following words within the grid. The words may be hidden horizontally, vertically, or diagonally and may appear backward or forward. Ignore words contained within parentheses.

ANTIQUITIES	DOCUMENTS	LOOTING
ARCHAEOLOGICAL SITES	EXPERT	MASTERPIECES
ART COLLECTORS	FENCING	MUSEUMS
ART CRIME TEAM	FORGERY	PRIVATE COLLECTIONS
ARTIFACTS	GALLERY	PROVENANCE
ART THEFT	GARDNER MUSEUM	RAPID DEPLOYMENT
AUCTION HOUSE	GRAVE PROTECTION	RECOVERY
AUTHENTICATE	HEIST	SECURITY SYSTEMS
BURIAL SITES	HISTORY	STOLEN ART FILE
COUNTERFEIT	INTERPOL	STOLEN PROPERTY
CULTURAL PROPERTY	INTERSTATE THEFT	VALUABLES
DATABASE	INVENTORY	

#37

ART THEFT

V K S L F G N I C N E F I N V E N T O R Y X U E U
K F J D N H G A R D N E R M U S E U M H W D O L S
W C I R R E T G R A V E P R O T E C T I O N H I F
R V T C V T N F N H G S H Z K N Z M W X J B Y F Y
H A R C H A E O L O G I C A L S I T E S Z R P T B
T I I P K C M X L F M T B E Z G Y B H J E E R R B
I N P R F I Y B O O D H E F W P L T H G G M I A U
E T H O J T O V R E T I K I C B T Z R G A V V N R
F E K V G N L V A S L S O O F L L O S E R A A E I
R R G E L E P A N A E T F R O O F D T E P R T L A
E S B N Z H E L T B X O S W O C O E C A Y T E O L
T T J A O T D U A A Y R W T N C M O D U T T C T S
N A H N P U D A R T H Y I I U I V U L C R H O S I
U T Y C V A I B T A E N W M R E F C O T E E L U T
O E O E D K P L I D G E E C R O E Q P I P F L E E
C T N M R Z A E F M X N T Y R K Y C R O O T E X S
A H P I Y P R S A Y T R W F W L T S E N R L C P E
U E R D E T S F C S A Z T G Z R P P T H P V T E L
Y F C O X B A N T I Q U I T I E S W N O N P I R U
R T V Y E N Y S S T X V A N F V U N I U E R O T G
E H C U L T U R A L P R O P E R T Y X S L A N V C
L Z E Y M A S T E R P I E C E S I H K E O L S I F
L V K I I E S M U E S U M X H F O E G H T Z J E Q
A C J A S R S E C U R I T Y S Y S T E M S P W R E
G V T S W T A V G O H A R T C O L L E C T O R S L

#38 CYBERCRIME

The FBI is the lead federal agency for investigating cyber-attacks and intrusions by criminals, overseas adversaries, and terrorists. Cyber intrusions are becoming more commonplace, more dangerous, and more sophisticated. Cyber criminals are computer geeks looking for bragging rights, businesses trying to gain an upper hand in the marketplace by hacking competitor websites, rings of criminals wanting to steal personal information to sell on the black market, and spies and terrorists looking to rob our nation of vital information or launch cyber strikes.

Locate and redact or circle the following words within the grid. The words may be hidden horizontally, vertically, or diagonally and may appear backward or forward. Ignore words contained within parentheses.

ANTIVIRUS
BACKUP DRIVE
BITCOIN
BLACK MARKET
BLOCK CHAIN
BOTS
BROWSERS
COMPUTERS
CYBERCRIME
CYBERSPACE
DARK WEB
DATA BREACH
DIGITAL DEVICES
EMAIL
ENCRYPTION
END USER
FIRMWARE
HACKER
IDENTITY THEFT
INFECTED
INFRASTRUCTURE
INTERCEPT
INTERNET
INTRUSION
MALICIOUS CODE
MALWARE
NETWORK
ONLINE THEFT
OPERATING SYSTEMS
PHISHING
RANSOMWARE
RCFL (Regional Computer Forensics Laboratories)
SMISHING
SOFTWARE
SPAM
WEBSITE

#38 CYBERCRIME

I N F R A S T R U C T U R E Q H J B K J E M A P S

U P P F D X J U P S Y E I D T S H I Z J R S M S C

F J T P P C Y B E R S P A C E Q S T K R A X Z Z I

I W O N L I N E T H E F T H T P N C A I W T M M V

R G N I H S I M S U R K S Q B I I O Z N T S X B M

M I E G M N H S C E B A C F J U X I K T F O J W E

W N R S R B R O W S E R S A T F Q N O E O Y Y V I

A F A M X Z Q B I X G B G S H J B H C R S F I H D

R E W E Q I L U P H X T R U U Y D A E C V R W S E

E C L T R N I A H C K C O L B R N O K E D S R L N

D T A S S G N I H S I H P D Y I I O N P I E H H T

Q E M Y D A T A B R E A C H J C X V U T T E T J I

Q D E S Z G Z H J E U G X K N J T K I U N V L P T

E E N G S R Q Z N J F I N Q N Q C B P T Y R F Y Y

D Y C N L L M D W I B E W K R A D M E J N S C K T

D Z R I Y N U U V U X T L B B S O Q M P A A R T H

Q T Y T T S G P V M V L P O J C D S I I K I Y E E

P G P A E F E R A W M O S N A R J A R W R W E N F

F G T R W L I V L V C P C C O Q E N C X G L Q R T

E K I E E T I S B E W B T T A J U H R T W P L E T

R H O P B L A C K M A R K E T P O E E F O S I T X

F U N O E D O C S U O I C I L A M G B W A P A N B

D I G I T A L D E V I C E S W D Q G Y F Z U M I F

S T O B D R H L Q O J S M J X J P Y C S A W E Y H

F G M X K R O W T E N A I N T R U S I O N U T K Q

#39 CIVIL RIGHTS

The FBI is the primary federal agency responsible for investigating allegations regarding violations of federal civil rights statutes related to Hate Crimes, Color of Law, and the Freedom of Access to Clinic Entrances (FACE) Act. These laws are designed to protect the civil rights of all persons--citizens and non-citizens alike--within U.S. territory.

Locate and redact or circle the following words within the grid. The words may be hidden horizontally, vertically, or diagonally and may appear backward or forward. Ignore words contained within parentheses.

ANTI-SEMITISM
BIAS
CHURCH BOMBINGS
CIVIL RIGHTS
CONSPIRACY
CROSS BURNINGS
EXCESSIVE FORCE
FACE (Freedom of Access to Clinic Entrances)
FAIR HOUSING
FALSE ARREST
GENOCIDE
HATE SPEECH
HUMAN RIGHTS
IGNORANCE
INTOLERANCE
NEO-NAZISM
OBSTRUCTION OF JUSTICE
POLICE BRUTALITY
POLICE MISCONDUCT
RACIALLY MOTIVATED
RACIAL PROFILING
SKINHEADS
SLAVE LABOR
TOP PRIORITY
UNDER COLOR OF LAW
VICTIM ASSISTANCE
WAR CRIMES
WHITE NATIONALISM
WHITE SUPREMACISTS

#39

CIVIL RIGHTS

M R B D Y G V I C T I M A S S I S T A N C E O Z F
H Y R T O P P R I O R I T Y C A R I P S N O C P B
U V T A X K Z X N D F W H O S U D W S A R B X S N
K B S F O N T R T W P H D J K Q Y A X W B S P G S
C U S B D P S G O O W I V J I M M L L H F T O N P
B D E Z C P E N L E M T F O N S J F T T P R L I J
R Y B Z X X R I E E M E G M H I D O J S R U I B E
F L I Y T M R S R P V S S W E T Z R C X A C C M I
M N U W U S A U A H M U R N A I N O J H C T E O H
E S W Q E I E O N X N P Y E D M G L L I I I M B A
C C A U X L S H C Z A R E O S E N O Y C A O I H C
X R A Z C A L R E P S E D N Y S M C Q I L N S C B
S O H F E N A I F M S M I A B I B R Q A P O C R S
T B A W S O F A E U I A C Z A T V E M A R F O U M
H A T A S I K F T B V C O I G N Z D S L O J N H G
G L E R I T J H D E R I N S L A W N P F F U D C F
I E S C V A V I A Z D S E M Y H J U E T I S U C C
R V P R E N N O F O T T G O N U G T G V L T C R J
N A E I F E X C R O S S B U R N I N G S I I T O M
A L E M O T J M L Q G A E D K T X W Z P N C O R E
M S C E R I H T O Y D S I H B K Z C B F G E I U B
U T H S C H X U H Q M H K B I G N O R A N C E C D
H Z R R E W V Q E P Q J S T H G I R L I V I C P I
P I R E J D E T A V I T O M Y L L A I C A R G G C
P O L I C E B R U T A L I T Y C E L C U F S U K O

#40 COUNTERINTELLIGENCE

The FBI has been responsible for identifying and neutralizing ongoing national security threats from foreign intelligence services, such as the Soviet Union and other communist nations during the Cold War. However, since the terrorist attacks of September 11, 2001, its mission is much broader. The FBI is the lead agency for exposing, preventing, and investigating intelligence activities on US soil. The Counterintelligence Division uses its full suite of investigative and intelligence capabilities to combat counterintelligence threats.

Locate and redact or circle the following words within the grid. The words may be hidden horizontally, vertically, or diagonally and may appear backward or forward. Ignore words contained within parentheses.

ARMS REGULATIONS

CHINA

CIA (Central Intelligence Agency)

CLASSIFIED MATERIAL

COUNTERINTELLIGENCE

CRITICAL ASSETS

DEAD DROP

DIRECTORATE

DISRUPT

ECONOMIC ESPIONAGE

ESPIONAGE

EXPLOIT

FISA ORDER (Foreign Intelligence Surveillance Act)

FOREIGN ADVERSARIES

FSB (Federal Security Service of the Russian Federation)

HOMELAND SECURITY

IDEOLOGY

INTEL COMMUNITY

INTELLIGENCE BRANCH

KGB (Soviet Union Security Agency)

MITIGATION

NATIONAL SECURITY

NSA (National Security Agency)

PENETRATION

PREVENTION

RUSSIA

RUSSIAN INTERFERENCE

SECURITY THREAT

SPIES

SUBVERSIVE ACTIVITIES

THREAT MATRIX

TOP SECRET

TRADECRAFT

TRADE SECRETS

WALK-IN

YEAR OF THE SPY

#40 COUNTERINTELLIGENCE

```
O T M F E X P L O I T E Y P M I T I G A T I O N S
B I S E C U R I T Y T H R E A T O L S O O K Z C M
Q H C N A R B E C N E G I L L E T N I A G X T R J
C L A S S I F I E D M A T E R I A L M B N M R I K
D L I E G A N O I P S E C I M O N O C E K B A T E
S A J J N A T I O N A L S E C U R I T Y X S D I F
U R U S S I A Q Y U S K L W Z E U V U C I F E C O
B T E R C E S P O T F Y G P U T A Z B F A V C A R
V B N G H Y P S E H T F O R A E Y S X H E B R L E
E U C O U N T E R I N T E L L I G E N C E X A A I
R Q F U P E N E T R A T I O N F P A J S I T F S G
S Q R U S S I A N I N T E R F E R E N C E P T S N
I B C D D M X Y T I N U M M O C L E T N I I K E A
V P Q X I O P O R D D A E D S U I W J Y P R P T D
E G M Q S P R E V E N T I O N S H D K P S M K S V
A E T Q R T M J F A K D V Z X P L W E J X L X W E
C R K R U B X I R T A M T A E R H T G O A X T S R
T O T L P A K W H V G C K Q J N M W G P L A H K S
I B R H T O N N I Z N I K L A W R F I I G O S P A
V B O W E E S P I O N A G E O P N Q A G N D G Y R
I U U S T E R C E S E D A R T Q Z P A N I H C Y I
T J Y T I R U C E S D N A L E M O H Q W M W M W E
I O I D A C I C V X F I S A O R D E R V S S W T S
E U N B G H E T A R O T C E R I D A K K E W P I S
S N O I T A L U G E R S M R A X B S P S K H Z H K
```

#41 AMERICAN SPIES

The following individuals were investigated by the FBI and its intelligence community counterparts for espionage, treason, and the improper handling of classified materials.

Locate and redact or circle the following words within the grid. The words may be hidden horizontally, vertically, or diagonally and may appear backward or forward. Ignore words contained within parentheses.

ALDRICH AMES	EDWARD SNOWDEN	MAKSIM MARTYNOV
ALGER HISS	ETHEL ROSENBERG	RICHARD MILLER
ANA MONTES	FREDERICK DUQUESNE	ROBERT HANSSEN
BRIAN REGAN	IVA TOGURI D'AQUINO	ROBERT LIPKA
CHELSEA MANNING	JOHN WALKER	ROD RAMSAY
CHRISTOPHER BOYCE	JONATHAN POLLARD	RONALD PELTON
CLAYTON LONETREE	JULIUS ROSENBERG	ROY OAKLEY
CLYDE LEE CONRAD	KURT LUDWIG	SHARON SCRANAGE
DAVID BOONE	LARRY WU-TAI CHIN	STEWART NOZETTE
EARL PITTS	LEONARDO MASCHERONI	

#41

AMERICAN SPIES

W G I W D U L T R U K E D W A R D S N O W D E N W
U B I S J G O R N E S S N A H T R E B O R U S H G
Y E L K A O Y O R O J I K K T V F X I I C I K C Z
E J N G R E B N E S O R S U I L U J B O L N Q R E
D L L S T E W A R T N O Z E T T E B L E A V G E R
Z I Y E C C H E L S E A M A N N I N G O Y W K K J
N A G E R N A I R B R Z A L T I Z H H H T J E L C
E N O O B D I V A D I L H R R N S S V X O I N A H
F F Y Y R J A B C R G I R E C O E D O U N V S W R
S N C U R R F V R E S O L K N R L A N D L A E N I
H O T E U N Y Z R H B L P E I E A R Y A O T U H S
A T Z X P X S H Z E I Q T X H H J N T N N O Q O T
R L B R F D I N R M S H Y H C C N O R A E G U J O
O E Q Z M S X T D G E M A V I S N C A M T U D V P
N P X F S G L R O L M D S R A A B E M O R R K N H
S D D U E I A E R T A Y M F T M F E M N E I C U E
C L I I P H U O Y Q H Q A N U O Z L I T E D I I R
R A Z K C U S R U M C C R C W D C E S E U A R T B
A N A I K E I G K P I R D A Y R S D K S D Q E J O
N O R W N B G S L D R M O S R A W Y A H O U D T Y
A R O B U R G V I I D B R B R N Q L M D L I E V C
G L E C Y E H P Y K L Q M Y A O N C Z I I N R Q E
E R J G N E Q U L S A J V R L E K B H F X O F V W
G A B O E A R L P I T T S N O L R Q J Y I S S W Z
Z L R K Q J O N A T H A N P O L L A R D H E R Q F

#42 NCIC DATABASE

The National Crime Information Center (NCIC) is an electronic clearinghouse of crime data. It is a computerized database containing documented criminal justice information with files on persons and properties. The information and records regarding arrests, charges, convictions, and sentences are entered by thousands of authorized law enforcement agencies. Law enforcement agencies around the country have access to the database 24 hours a day.

Locate and redact or circle the following words within the grid. The words may be hidden horizontally, vertically, or diagonally and may appear backward or forward. Ignore words contained within parentheses.

BACKGROUND CHECKS

CJIS (Criminal Justice Information Services Division)

CRIMINAL HISTORIES

DATABASE

FINGERPRINTS

FOREIGN FUGITIVES

FUGITIVES

HOST COMPUTER

HUMAN REMAINS

IDENTITY THEFT

IMMIGRATION VIOLATORS

LICENSE PLATES

MISSING PERSONS

NCIC

PROTECTION THREATS

RECOVERED GUNS

SECURITIES

SEXUAL OFFENDERS

STOLEN BOATS

STOLEN WEAPONS

SUPERVISED RELEASE

TERRORIST GROUPS

UCR (Uniform Crime Report)

UNIDENTIFIED PERSONS

VEHICLE IDENTIFICATION

VIOLENT GANGS

WANTED PERSONS

#42 NCIC DATABASE

Q D F O R E I G N F U G I T I V E S A R C E A E I

C O R N R V I O L E N T G A N G S H E X Y K D G D

O J Y E X G E S A E L E R D E S I V R E P U S R E

D Y I H U M A N R E M A I N S B R K D L B Z G K N

S N O S R E P G N I S S I M N X F M D R F N I C T

F D J S T A E R H T N O I T C E T O R P N D C B I

W V L V E H I C L E I D E N T I F I C A T I O N T

F U A Z F S R E D N E F F O L A U X E S Y N E O Y

C P I Y M S E I R O T S I H L A N I M I R C K M T

X U L G C I C N Y S P U O R G T S I R O R R E T H

J X O Y V S E G B E S A B A T A D J E E U E T X E

G S N O S R E P D E I F I T N E D I N U G F E B F

S Z G M X E W C V Q E H L S T O L E N B O A T S T

T O N V W L A I K G I X M T L D E H R P R N G B W

N K R C B Q T V B S K C E H C D N U O R G K C A B

I P X B S I P H J W L F W Y V E M N B T A P L B M

R T F U G M Q L F J Z U K H H P R S O X Y U D L R

P H C U F S Y E B I Q F S N O P A E W N E L O T S

R R F P O K H N C Q X W A N T E D P E R S O N S R

E C S E C U R I T I E S E T A L P E S N E C I L G

G I M M I G R A T I O N V I O L A T O R S B N O X

N W V I E C R R Y B C Y H Y M B H R D F S S F J F

I L G A R E T U P M O C T S O H D A F P T R U C I

F S D N O Y P I F O V R E C O V E R E D G U N S S

L P V P X I W E Q M C T V R N Y W M E P D K T P N

#43 CRIMES AGAINST CHILDREN

The FBI provides a rapid and effective investigative response to reported federal crimes involving child victims. Crimes against Children (CAC) investigators provide investigative, technical, and resource assistance to state and local law enforcement during the most critical time period following a child abduction. It is for this reason that when a child 12 years or younger is missing or abducted, the FBI has been authorized to initiate an investigation even if there is no known interstate aspect.

Locate and redact or circle the following words within the grid. The words may be hidden horizontally, vertically, or diagonally and may appear backward or forward. Ignore words contained within parentheses.

AMBER ALERT

CAC

CARD TEAM (Child Abduction Rapid Deployment)

CHILD ABDUCTOR

CHILD PORNOGRAPHY

CHILD SUPPORT RECOVERY

CRITICAL HOURS

CUSTODY DISPUTE

DISTRIBUTION

ENDANGERED CHILD

EVIDENCE CONCEALMENT

EXPLICIT

EXPLOITATION

HARD DRIVE

HUMAN TRAFFICKING

INNOCENT IMAGES

INTERNET

KIDNAPPING

MISSING CHILDREN

MOLESTERS

OFFENDERS

ONLINE PREDATORS

PARENTAL KIDNAPPING

PEDOPHILE

POSSESSION

PROJECT SAFE CHILDHOOD

PROSTITUTION

RESCUE

SEX ABUSE IMAGES

SEX TOURISM

SEXUAL ASSAULT

THUMB DRIVE

UNDERGROUND NETWORK

VICTIMIZATION

WEBCAM

#43 CRIMES AGAINST CHILDREN

E V B H P E V I R D D R A H Y O R G J E X R Z E R

K E G N I K C I F F A R T N A M U H R F Z C L W B

E O L B K T N E M L A E C N O C E C N E D I V E O

K K D H I R N O I T U T I T S O R P J J V X Y C P

E K L C Y U T C S C A C L U G D O X C K E F H L P

U K I C P W U U D I S T R I B U T I O N N J P R R

C N H I A E V I R D B M U H T J M A E T D R A C O

S T C C J R I Y H K L T Q E X P L I C I T P R P J

E E D U N D E R G R O U N D N E T W O R K H G A E

R X E G W K F I N N O C E N T I M A G E S G O R C

E P R S R U O H L A C I T I R C D K N A Z O N E T

I L E E H J L E D U N O I S S E S S O P X C R N S

K O G L N K B G P E D O P H I L E Y A Y J H O T A

Z I N G M N R Z L G D S R E T S E L O M W I P A F

Z T A G C N E R D L I H C G N I S S I M A L D L E

J A D C A T A B A M S I R U O T X E S O M D L K C

M T N V K W S E X A B U S E I M A G E S B A I I H

K I E W O N L I N E P R E D A T O R S U E B H D I

E O Y F J O V I C T I M I Z A T I O N R R D C N L

Z N T L U A S S A L A U X E S I V Q P J A U Z A D

E T U P S I D Y D O T S U C X Z X Y D J L C D P H

I B M T E N R E T N I X Y M A C B E W X E T U P O

M O F F E N D E R S K C Q G D Q C F R P R O R I O

K J G N I P P A N D I K T E D K R B R M T R Y N D

L S Y R E V O C E R T R O P P U S D L I H C A G S

#44 ORGANIZED CRIME (LCN)

Italian-American organized crime is known as La Cosa Nostra (LCN), the mafia, or simply the mob. Members are associated with "families" located primarily in large cities, and engage in various illegal activities to earn money.

Locate and redact or circle the following words within the grid. The words may be hidden horizontally, vertically, or diagonally and may appear backward or forward. Ignore words contained within parentheses.

ASSOCIATES
BLOOD TIES
BONANNO
BOOKMAKING
CAPO
CAPTAIN
CASINO SKIMMING
CHICAGO OUTFIT
CODE OF CONDUCT
COLOMBO
DECAVALCANTE
EXTORTION
FAMILIES
GAMBINO
GAMBLING
GENOVESE
HIT MAN
LABOR UNIONS
LA COSA NOSTRA
LOAN SHARK
LUCCHESE
MADE MAN
MAFIA
MOB BOSS
NEW ENGLAND MOB
PHILLY MOB
PROTECTION RACKET
RACKETEERING
RICO (Racketeer Influenced and Corrupt Organizations)
SECRET SOCIETIES
SICILY
SOLDIER
SYNDICATE
THIS THING OF OURS
UNDERWORLD

#44 ORGANIZED CRIME (LCN)

Q S E I T D O O L B M H N K C A P O Q S Y S Z C K
R A P G G L T C U D N O C F O E D O C R R I M Z O
A W L L F I S N O I N U R O B A L Q I I I C A F Q
C U C N M S U F B M Y W D N U U J S K C X I D D I
K H E S J F B B F E S E H C C U L T H J Q L E E U
E M P S Y B U N D E R W O R L D T O G R M Y M C P
T M P Z E I Y L N H R E I D L O S Q A X F H A A I
E N J E H V M Q S Z H N I A T P A C M F P G N V I
E A E V I A O Y W O L L S M G L U D B J X B D A P
R S M Q F N M N C K M E O C N O P W I B M O X L Y
I M I I N G Z I E S Z B X H I A R Z N O S O E C B
N U A A W P R S F G B U K N L N C H O M V K T A O
G C N W W W B G L O L Y M Y B S K N D Y Q M A N Y
F O I A M X K P S Q O K J C M H C K V L F A C T M
B S W W D B F S K O H D I Y A A F E C L D K I E S
M H U H I O B M O L O C R S G R G F H I R I D X E
J J O S E T A I C O S S A Q T K X V G H U N N U I
E C P Y Q H A R T S O N A S O C A L H P R G Y I L
F H Y Q S E C R E T S O C I E T I E S C B Y S D I
A E Q X T O N E Y O C H I C A G O O U T F I T R M
F H C A S I N O S K I M M I N G I V J R D S R K A
S R U O F O G N I H T S I H T N A M T I H A K Y F
O Y L Q K S M N E W E N G L A N D M O B O V U V B
D X L N O I T R O T X E N C T S S P M A X L O Z Y
T E K C A R N O I T C E T O R P J G S A U R J U C

#45 ORGANIZED CRIME (TRANSNATIONAL)

Transnational Organized Crime (TOC) members may have ethnic or cultural ties to Europe, Africa, Asia, and the Middle East. The primary goal of these organizations is to generate money through illegal schemes that target victims all over the world.

Locate and redact or circle the following words within the grid. The words may be hidden horizontally, vertically, or diagonally and may appear backward or forward. Ignore words contained within parentheses.

AFRICA
ART THEFT
ASIA
BALKAN CLANS
BLACK MARKET
BORDER SECURITY
BRIBERY
CENTRAL AMERICAN GANGS
CIGARETTE SMUGGLING
CORRUPTION
COUNTERFEIT GOODS
CRIME FAMILY
CRIMINALIZED TONGS

CYBERCRIMES
DARK WEB
DISMANTLE
DISRUPT
DRUG TRAFFICKING
ENTERPRISES
EUROPE
EXTORTION
FRAUD SCHEMES
GAMBLING
HONG KONG TRIADS
HUMAN TRAFFICKING
MIDDLE EAST

MIGRANT SMUGGLING
MONEY LAUNDERING
OLIGARCHS
PREDICATE OFFENSES
PROSTITUTION
RACKETEERING
RANSOMWARE
RICO ACT (Racketeer Influenced and Corrupt Organizations)
SAFE HAVEN COUNTRIES
SLAVERY
THIEVES IN LAW
TOC (Transnational Organized Crime)

#45

ORGANIZED CRIME (TRANSNATIONAL)

R I C O A C T P Q I C Y B E R C R I M E S Z Y Q A
K T U H Z J Z D R U G T R A F F I C K I N G C L X
W Q Y R E B I R B N S N N T E K R A M K C A L B T
S P H S G N A G N A C I R E M A L A R T N E C M F
D I S R U P T S F R S H C R A G I L O E F G W I E
S E I R T N U O C N E V A H E F A S N S S T P D H
S E X M T S V A F R I C A R N R O S O R M X R D T
M B T I T E K U C E B C Q K R X U T I O P S E L T
O A D G C S C R I M E F A M I L Y Q T H G D D E R
N A J R R I S S G Z W R G B A C W E P U S A I E A
E I W A I R Q F A I P L N L W O C O U M N I C A R
Y S Q N M P C T R Y F V I A X U Z B R A A R A S N
L A R T I R F P E T A G R Y N N P I R N L T T T A
A U A S N E R O T I C W E R C T R B O T C G E G M
U N N M A T A B T R S A E E M E O D C R N N O D E
N N S U L N U E E U A L T V C R S D P A A O F S Q
D O O G I E D Z S C G N E A U F T I A F K K F R D
E I M G Z B S U M E A I K L E E I S Q F L G E H P
R T W L E Z C U U S M S C S P I T M G I A N N K Q
I R A I D I H C G R B E A Z O T U A L C B O S P K
N O R N T Q E O G E L V R F R G T N D K D H E O U
G T E G O W M T L D I E X J U O I T O I X R S V S
B X A N N L E Z I R N I A L E O O L V N G M S R X
S E N W G B S R N O G H Z I A D N E T G Q X C J E
X H T S S I Z O G B I T Q V N S D A R K W E B L P

#46 ARREST AND SEARCH WARRANTS

The most common circumstance for danger is when an agent executes arrest or search warrants. Therefore, planning and preparation are paramount to all FBI tactical operations. After obtaining a warrant, FBI case agents draft a written contingency action plan based on Bureau Standard Operating Procedures (SOP) or guidelines for the execution of all arrests and searches. The plan allows agents to consider and anticipate possible outcomes.

Locate and redact or circle the following words within the grid. The words may be hidden horizontally, vertically, or diagonally and may appear backward or forward. Ignore words contained within parentheses.

AFFIANT
AFFIDAVIT
ARRAIGNMENT
ARREST RECORD
ARREST TEAM
AUSA (Assistant US Attorney)
CAR STOPS
CHARGING DOCUMENTS
COMMAND POST
CRIMINAL HISTORY
DEBRIEF
DISTRICT COURT
EVIDENCE
FBI CUSTODY
FINGERPRINT
HANDCUFFS
INFORMANTS
INITIAL APPEARANCE
MAGISTRATE
MIRANDA WARNINGS
MUGSHOT
NONCOMPLIANT
OPERATIONS PLAN
PREDICATION
PRELIMINARY HEARING
PROBABLE CAUSE
REPORT OF INTERVIEW
SEARCH LOG
SOP (Standard Operating Procedures)
STAGING SITE
TAKEDOWN
TASK FORCE
TEAM LEADER
TRANSCRIPTS
UNDER SEAL
USAO (US Attorney's Office)

#46 ARREST AND SEARCH WARRANTS

O I M W I T T N Y D I S T R I C T C O U R T M J U
A G Q Z N S K K E D R R Y A P X B M U G S H O T A
S J D C I O E U K Q O T E T N E M N G I A R R A A
U S O S T P R R G O F T A A S H N S J N I E J E B
D X L P I D C E C H C T S T Q I O R Y D N T L A T
S Y S R A N W P L A K J N U U P P W T N A Z F E Q
P C S E L A U O A K G A P P C Q H O P K L F A L O
O R G L A M N R Y X M I R C D I Z X E O I M Q H Y
T I N I P M E T Q R T T O A C W B D G A L I U C D
S M I M P O W O O H N G B R R O O F N E X E E K C
R I N I E C L F G Z A L A R L W W T A L X T T H E
A N R N A U N I O Q I A B E N N C D E B R I E F V
C A A A R I B N L D L E L S T A E M C Y V S W E I
S L W R A J C T H A P S E T T R R R L A K G B Q D
P H A Y N B K E C U M R C R P R C R D S E N O W E
R I D H C Y S R R S O E A E U H A I E F P I L S N
E S N E E G A V A A C D U C B T F N O S U G P P C
D T A A A A R I E S N N S O I F I A S L T A K H E
I O R R F K A E S L O U E R A J X P W C N T K E P
C R I I Y D X W K K N L J D H B G V A B R S E S M
A Y M N V T N I R P R E G N I F O P R I W I Y A J
T B S G U Q D D R G H A N D C U F F S E K K P C M
I O V X Y P C M A G I S T R A T E C F Y O A J T R
O P E R A T I O N S P L A N E C R O F K S A T K S
N U I Y S W S Z S T N E M U C O D G N I G R A H C

#47 TRIALS AND COURT PROCEEDINGS

During a criminal trial, the federal prosecutor, known as the Assistant United States Attorney (AUSA), is in charge of presenting the government's case. However, because FBI case agents have been intimately involved in developing the facts and gathering the evidence presented in the indictment or information filed against the defendant, they are customarily seated next to the AUSA at the prosecutive table. Federal case law recognizes case agents as part of the legal team.

Locate and redact or circle the following words within the grid. The words may be hidden horizontally, vertically, or diagonally and may appear backward or forward. Ignore words contained within parentheses.

ACQUITTAL
AUSA
CASE LAW
CIVIL COURT
CONVICTION
COURTROOM
CRIMINAL TRIAL
CROSS EXAMINE
DEFENDANT
DEFENSE ATTORNEY
DISTRICT COURT
DOJ (Department of Justice)
EXPERT WITNESS
FACT WITNESS
GRAND JURY
GUILTY PLEA
HEARING
INDICTMENT
INFORMATION
JUDGE
JURY POOL
MAGISTRATE
MARSHALS SERVICE
PRE-TRIAL SERVICES
PROSECUTION TEAM
SENTENCING GUIDELINES
SEQUESTERED
TESTIMONY
TRIAL PREP
TRUE BILL
USAO (US Attorney's Office)
VERDICT
VOIR DIRE
WITNESS STAND

#47 TRIALS AND COURT PROCEEDINGS

T B R M A R S H A L S S E R V I C E D G F W P R X
Y W Y J R B Q K O D D E D N V W A L E N J H Q W P
L O O P Y R U J U F K N E R C V M C N T F I G Q R
N T R U E B I L L V A T F R M L A B I Q H D T B E
A I G F V C V R N H C E E A A D G Q M N I R R P T
F O R I U W X I A J Q N N Y B H I R A I N T U S R
F C L W A Z Y O V Z U C S P M R S A X Y F U O M I
V O I R D I R E L T I I E M S F T L E G O C C I A
Y R U J D N A R G I T N A X V T R W S U R O T Q L
C C A S E L A W F N T G T Q S G A L S I M N C T S
M I K L G S F O S D A G T C E U T Z O L A V I N E
A X V W H V I J A I L U O R H G E V R T T I R A R
E F S I P H Z Z Q C D I R I H Y D E C Y I C T D V
T P S T L G B X P T S D N M E J X U G P O T S N I
N E E N G C P M O M E E E I A T G E J L N I I E C
O R N E T Y O G N E Q L Y N R B C N K E W O D F E
I P T S J K K U D N U I Z A I L L U D A U N A E S
T L I S I R X J R T E N O L N K O B T N T B Z D K
U A W S O B S D B T S E V T G Q W F N E Y T G U E
C I T T S K Z F V C T S A R W Z M O O R T R U O C
E R C A Q N L J Q I E A Q I J K S K K S R B Y J M
S T A N L J F O P Q R S I A G O V I B T O M A W D
O L F D I E F D W X E U U L N B V K M A J B V J Q
R T C I D R E V R R D A T E S T I M O N Y J Z F F
P C U S A O N I H S S E N T I W T R E P X E Q E Y

#48 RADIO ALPHABET

The FBI operates the largest fixed land mobile radio system in the US. The following combinations of words are often used to distinguish specific letters when communicating by radio to ensure that messages are understood.

Locate and redact or circle the following words within the grid. The words may be hidden horizontally, vertically, or diagonally and may appear backward or forward. Ignore words contained within parentheses.

ALFA	JULIET	SIERRA
BRAVO	KILO	TANGO
CHARLIE	LIMA	UNIFORM
DELTA	MIKE	VICTOR
ECHO	NOVEMBER	WHISKEY
FOXTROT	OSCAR	X-RAY
GOLF	PAPA	YANKEE
HOTEL	QUEBEC	ZULU
INDIA	ROMEO	

#48

RADIO ALPHABET

H A K M O Q V K Q V G L P U V V E D I X P X E H A

V Q L A G O A E U R F Z L K A G R O T C I V C O B

M W O F K L Y I O L I K V M M O P Z W H D C L T A

U C D C A V E B E T U K V K L D X F J O K H T P W

I E E U B L P T S C J Z S H H P N B T A Y K B M Q

O B M L B J R J O P H H W V I V W S P P J A M J L

A E B D D D O K E H Q O Q A G G Z A I V T S R S U

G U D B V L Z T Q J U L I E T J P O E M O R O D O

K Q R B P N J I Y U G E Y R W P C W O X W R F H P

F X Z H R D V T V M B Q O E E K N A Y F J V I L L

T Y N B E K Y W X T W C N O V E M B E R M H N X C

C W S N C Q U Y N A J M P S G A W M S L L X U J B

D S P I V G Y Q J N F E N M I J R H J F U Z Z A S

S U S V A J J A V G Z S A S Z E Y T V O A N A W A

G L S O M V L C R O Y C K O B K R A U X Q T A F O

H I J E V L Q S J P Z H L S Z E R R M T J Z L H O

O Y X E B I Z I Y D D A V C H L O S A R W G X E C

W Y D C I F L O G N R R M A L W T O L O Q T R A D

I A K F N C N Y M I T L F R M D D N P T Z P C C E

R R K W D K M E O X C I O K R E M B P K G H R E J

P X N K I W A K N J X E H T K Y J O V A R B O O Z

P M Z S A N Q S K T J N A I C N C J S Y L X S O E

A Z K Y F Z V I V L H X M N P V T H Z Q T I F T B

J A L W U Y B H A L W Z V P N P T I Q O Y X M F C

O X H P K Y H W Y I K Z P J M J F W T K W B N A U

#49 CASE AND INFORMATION MANAGEMENT

The FBI's Information Management Division not only oversees the records of the Bureau but also provides some key services to law enforcement and to the American people. It responds to a large number of Freedom of Information and Privacy Act (FOIPA) requests every year from the news media, private citizens, and others around the world. The division maintains a high-tech electronic reading room called the Vault, that contains nearly 7,000 FBI digital records and other media that can be searched and read.

Locate and redact or circle the following words within the grid. The words may be hidden horizontally, vertically, or diagonally and may appear backward or forward. Ignore words contained within parentheses.

APPROVAL PROCESS
AUDIBLE RECORD
CASE FILE
CASE MANAGEMENT
CLASSIFIED
CLOSED CASE
DEADLINE
DIGITAL COPIES
DISPOSITION
DISSEMINATE
ELECTRONIC RECORD
FILE NUMBER
FOIPA (Freedom of Information and Privacy Act)
IMMEDIATE
INDEX
LEADS
LIBRARY
LINK ANALYSIS
MEDIA SCANNED
METADATA
NAME CHECKS
PENDING INACTIVE
POCATELLO DATA CENTER
PRECEDENCE
PRELIMINARY INQUIRY
PRIORITY
QUERY
READING ROOM
RECORDS
REDACT
REPORT OF INTERVIEW
REPOSITORIES
ROUTINE
SEARCHABLE
SENTINEL
THE VAULT
WEBSITE

#49

CASE AND INFORMATION MANAGEMENT

```
O Y W E I V R E T N I F O T R O P E R Q A V I Z T
R E P O S I T O R I E S U U R C S D A E L F I D S
U E X B N T C A D E R Y T P N I D E N I L D A E D
Q A E I M M E D I A T E Z V N X E D D G S Y L J G
Q M M H R D W S O R N O I T I S O P S I D X E P O
Y Q F R E T N E C A T A D O L L E T A C O P N E F
B N N F I T P U T N E M E G A N A M E S A C I N I
A W P R E L I M I N A R Y I N Q U I R Y P E T D L
I U E A P N L R E A D I N G R O O M Y R E N N I E
G S D H G C F A T A D A T E M Q A U H P L I E N N
I C E I S S E C O R P L A V O R P P A Y E T S G U
Y Y A A B N X B C E T I S B E W T E T A C U D I M
E Y S S R L N A R L Q R T L U A V E H T T O I N B
C S R K E C E Q I Z A V D B F Y W R I Z R R G A E
N Y A A C F H R U R I S W F N L Z M X R O K I C R
E Q D C R E I A E E E N S U H F Q T H O N I T T M
D N I B D B H L B C R C Y I D A O C A B I N A I G
E F Y Y D E I C E L O Y O K F H P N N C C D L V A
C F T S A Y S L E I E R S R Q I H I Y S R E C E F
E Y I A K L U O O M E P D H D L E J O W E X O P D
R K R E J J Z R L D A R H J T S N D J F C S P F N
P G O E H V I E O C S N P T J X U O V V O K I U X
O G I X Y B B H L I N K A N A L Y S I S R T E B R
H E R L J U F D I S S E M I N A T E F P D T S U F
Q R P U G H G W S N X D E N N A C S A I D E M C P
```

#50 LEGAL ATTACHE PROGRAM

The FBI stations agents and support personnel in legal attaché offices around the world to help protect Americans back home by building relationships with principal law enforcement, intelligence, and security services overseas. This collaboration ensures a prompt and continuous exchange of information and an immediate response to global events. The agents, referred to as Legats, are the FBI director's personal representatives abroad.

Locate and redact or circle the following words within the grid. The words may be hidden horizontally, vertically, or diagonally and may appear backward or forward. Ignore words contained within parentheses.

AMBASSADOR
ATTACHE
CHIEF OF MISSION
CIA (Central Intelligence Agency)
CLEARANCE
COOPERATION
COORDINATE
CULTURAL PROTOCOL
DIPLOMATIC COVER
DIRECTOR'S REPRESENTATIVE
EMBASSY
EXECUTIVE ORDER
EXTRATERRITORIAL
FBI ABROAD
FOREIGN POLICE
GLOBAL PRESENCE
HOST COUNTRY
INTERNATIONAL AFFAIRS
INTERPOL
IOD (International Operations Division)
JURISDICTION
LANGUAGE ABILITY
LEGAT
LIAISON
MARINE CONTINGENT
MUTUAL AGREEMENT
OVERSEAS POSTINGS
PROTECTION
RSO (Regional Security Officer)
SECURITY SERVICES
SOVEREIGNTY
STATE DEPARTMENT
SUB-OFFICES
TOUR OF DUTY
TREATIES
US CONSULATES

#50 LEGAL ATTACHE PROGRAM

T N E M E E R G A L A U T U M Q I N T E R P O L L

T T O U R O F D U T Y E M K C Y E X I X H C G L U

A S T A T E D E P A R T M E N T H O S Z L D L T S

G O S U S C O N S U L A T E S Y V M B E A I L I I

E D S U D A V G J H T N Y G X G I A A S I R A E O

L E G R B H Z D X O J I N V K K S R E Q N E I Z I

C P C W L O O T F W L D Z C M O A C Q O L C R C B

S T F N F A F S L R P R R Y U N U A I E K T O I P

G N O S E T N F T N A O W Y C R P S C A Y O T A R

N E R O N S X G I C V O Q E I M S H C M L R I H E

I G E V N O E C U C O C A T H I X R T B O S R J V

T N I E Y O I R Y A E U Y T M M Q Y R A C R R T O

S I G R C Z S T P B G S N F T O B L E S O E E L C

O T N E D L J I A L E E O T L A C D A S T P T N C

P N P I X L R N A R A F A F R P C Z T A O R A O I

S O O G K M J V V I E B M B D Y N H I D R E R I T

A C L N B R V I A I L P O J I Y F M E O P S T T A

E I T C X C J H U F B O L D L R Y S R L E X C M

S E C Y R E F C T T X G K O G G I A Z I A N E I O

R N E P S Q F B X Y J M Q D C I B T D Y R T K D L

E I J U E K K N O I T C E T O R P Y Y H U A V S P

V R E D R O E V I T U C E X E I K E H K T T T I I

O A D L L T J D A O R B A I B F Z X X M L I R R D

H M X Y S S A B M E G R R A Q P B V I O U V M U G

I N T E R N A T I O N A L A F F A I R S C E V J Q

#51 OVERSEAS OFFICES (A THRU K)

The FBI has 63 legal attaché offices--commonly known as legats--and more than two dozen smaller sub-offices in key cities around the globe, providing coverage for more than 180 countries, territories, and islands. Each office is established through mutual agreement with the host country and is situated in the U.S. embassy or consulate in that nation. Most of these offices are staffed with only two or three agents, and one or two support personnel.

Locate and redact or circle the following words within the grid. The words may be hidden horizontally, vertically, or diagonally and may appear backward or forward. Ignore words contained within parentheses.

ABU DHABI
ABUJA
ACCRA
ADDIS ABABA
AMMAN
ANKARA
ATHENS
BAGHDAD
BANGKOK
BEIJING
BELGRADE
BERLIN
BERN
BOGOTA
BRASILIA
BRIDGETOWN
BRUSSELS
BUCHAREST
BUDAPEST
BUENOS AIRES
CAIRO
CANBERRA
COPENHAGEN
DAKAR
DHAKA
DOHA
HONG KONG
ISLAMABAD
JAKARTA
KABUL
KUALA LUMPUR
KYIV

#51 OVERSEAS OFFICES (A THRU K)

```
F W M C I Y L U B A K N Z S J S K Y D Z T T D Z D
W P B U C H A R E S T P D W Y Z N Z J M V T S O G
Y H V S L E S S U R B S A Z C W W E D G H M N G T
V S E R I A S O N E U B D A N B A Q H S P E J Z K
B R I D G E T O W N E M W P N S J X B T M Y K Z U
D T T S Z Q Q M D A D H G A B K L C T A A P E N A
F H O N F O R D A Y K A O N X P A A M U V K E K L
H H Y I S Z N A W N B T W Z O W B R R T Y T W H A
C V I L D S L B D T X Z I Y P A L T A F Y J C V L
G B V R H A M A X Q E O Y A B A X M S W B O O W U
H M Y E A I F M H V T Y C A N S M V G O P V Q T M
K C M B K L V A M P Y C S R B A N W E E T A G B P
M W B O A I L L T A R I D A N O K H N X Z E V E U
D O H A N S C S X A D A N B C J E H I T P T J I R
S N G R R A K I Q D A G X H O G A B Z F Z K X J S
G O E C I R N P A Q K T W Q V G E C J W Y S K I G
I B E R T B F T L O D T H D E L O Z S Y W Y S N B
S M O L A B F M K G U B A N G A T T K B I O O G Q
B I N S W T U Q R Y V K K R B I F Q A V Y V Z X U
J W K X M U R C K R A M A U J K O E Q Y J K E V H
B V M G V E A A E R C D D Y K E U B U D A P E S T
F T A J U B A Q K K E H B Y H O N G K O N G U J Z
F P L V E P S O L A A V B N H B X R R Q B G O N Y
F U Z W H Y I G B B J X C Q X V Z Z L M N M P D G
X S S T K I T D I C A N B E R R A K R Q F A F S K
```

#52 OVERSEAS OFFICES (L THRU Z)

The FBI has 63 legal attaché offices--commonly known as legats--and more than two dozen smaller sub-offices in key cities around the globe, providing coverage for more than 180 countries, territories, and islands. Each office is established through mutual agreement with the host country and is situated in the U.S. embassy or consulate in that nation. Most of these offices are staffed with only two or three agents, and one or two support personnel.

Locate and redact or circle the following words within the grid. The words may be hidden horizontally, vertically, or diagonally and may appear backward or forward. Ignore words contained within parentheses.

LONDON	PARIS	SEOUL
MADRID	PHNOM PENH	SOFIA
MANILA	PRAGUE	TBILISI
MEXICO CITY	PRETORIA	TEL AVIV
MOSCOW	RABAT	THE HAGUE
MUSCAT	RIGA	TOKYO
NAIROBI	RIYADH	TUNIS
NEW DELHI	ROME	VIENNA
NUR SULTAN	SAN SALVADOR	WARSAW
OTTAWA	SANTIAGO	
PANAMA CITY	SANTO DOMINGO	

#52 OVERSEAS OFFICES (L THRU Z)

G D J J O C Y V H J H O J L K G Y O B H N D N V S

D O Z S B P I T L V U W L Y S I R A P I S R Y L P

O H V J G E V H I A B T I Z P D E S H Q F E Z C D

G G U W T M P O L C Z W H P W C T O K Y O V O Y W

S L N L Z T A Z R E A H A H M G R R T N R R L U Y

N I M I A S B D N N D M P S G B T D L A W T F I L

A O V F M G A G R D L W A Y R N K M X T X G Q Y K

D A D M L O V N R I V I E N N A Y Y K L N P Y X T

E I V N P N D M T J D S V N A M W F S U F H M A B

C F N D O B R O J I V S D F A P T E G S T N O T I

M O J I X L G V T S A E N O U R M U Z R K O S H L

O S N B U L F K G N K G T T D O V W S U D M C E I

D H U O Y U W G S T A W O T R J Y F J N A P O H S

B D M R H W I A C H V S H A J U V I Z I T E W A I

F A C I J D L O A A T V W W Y S R S D W F N V G K

F Y Y A L V H M U L L I V A K E Z N T G K H D U E

V I V N A G L A T I M Z K J P D E A M O A Y U E K

H R Y D P P S F F N I Q X K M T B G O Z A J P Y A

F E O Z H C L V F A R X S P Z A A P M A V V F G I

G R O F V K V B Z M W J O I R E M C F K I Z P F R

H Q M D W A N L B Y U Z F T N T U C S V B T J U O

E A G C M E X I C O C I T Y O U M R A U M L K O T

Q X G V O P T D R F H Z U D E X T L D U M K S C E

J F F I K D K K O K I A Z R K E E E U G A R P C R

K F E B R Y J O C V K D X R I T W C T H E K S K P

#53 LANGUAGE ANALYSTS

FBI linguists and analysts use their knowledge of other cultures and languages to help the FBI fulfill its mission to protect the United States from threats both international and domestic. The success of the FBI's mission is dependent upon high quality language services and the ability to translate and analyze information in a timely manner. FBI Language Analysts begin their careers as Contract Linguists.

Locate and redact or circle the following words within the grid. The words may be hidden horizontally, vertically, or diagonally and may appear backward or forward. Ignore words contained within parentheses.

- ARABIC
- CAREER OPPORTUNITIES
- CHINESE
- CONTRACT LINGUISTS
- CRITICAL LANGUAGES
- CULTURAL EXPERTISE
- ENGLISH
- FARSI
- FOREIGN DIGNITARY
- GLOBAL SOCIETY
- INTERPRETING
- JAPANESE
- KOREAN
- LANGUAGE TEST
- LISTENING
- NATIVE SPEAKER
- NVTC (National Virtual Translation Center)
- OVERSEAS ASSIGNMENT
- PASHTO
- PROFICIENCY
- READING
- RUSSIAN
- SCREENING
- SKILLS
- SPANISH
- SPEAKING
- TESTS
- TRANSCRIPTS
- TRANSLATE DOCUMENT
- TRANSLATOR
- TRAVEL OPPORTUNITIES
- URDU
- VIETNAMESE

#53

LANGUAGE ANALYSTS

S T Q C T Z W C C U L T U R A L E X P E R T I S E
Y E R W A Y G N I D A E R T W F H S E M T P J N S
Z K I A R C R C A F L O N V N N H Q A N W E U C S
M G K T N G O X V U A G L H P V O I J L G Z S O F
L C L X I S V N E X M I N N D T F P P G V L R T M
R A I O T N L M T S V X C I P C Y W Z F M C I H S
C U S L B S U A F R E W P X N Y K S O L W A T S X
T V E S R A K T T P A M R V T E P A S H T O P E H
S V G G O Z L Q R E R C A J H Q T D H N H L N K Y
E S A H T G U S K O D O T N K U C S C D S I A R S
T T U X A N C C O J P O F L T U R Q I G I B E V N
E P G N L I K P Q C C P C I I E H O B L N D R B A
G I N L S N D J P J I H O U C N I Y A O A X O Z I
A R A G N E A R M W G E I L M I G V R E P N K B S
U C L N A E H X W L N R T N E E E U A G S K P K S
G S L X R R E U D G I Y B Y E V N N I X N J H T U
N N A E T C V W S J K U R D U S A T C S G K J R R
A A C G B S O T H J A P A N E S E R F Y T F Z M D
L R I F U N A T I V E S P E A K E R T N R S S F C
U T T S K Y Q E T U P C C A S L L I K S T H Z Z F
T Q I D F K Y T W X S B G C Z R D D M H L S Y S P
X U R Y E C A R E E R O P P O R T U N I T I E S D
F G C O V E R S E A S A S S I G N M E N T F D F O
Y R A T I N G I D N G I E R O F F A R S I T A P A
S W Z N A P Y Q V G N I T E R P R E T N I L Y W H

#54 FINGERPRINT IDENTIFICATION

Because of their uniqueness and consistency over time, fingerprints have been used for identification for over a century. Due to technological advances in recent years, the process has become more automated and expeditious. The FBI's Integrated Automated Fingerprint Identification System (IAFIS), is a state of the art system that accepts and processes digital fingerprint submissions. The national database of fingerprint features is maintained at the Criminal Justice Information Services Division (CJIS) in Clarksburg, West Virginia.

Locate and redact or circle the following words within the grid. The words may be hidden horizontally, vertically, or diagonally and may appear backward or forward. Ignore words contained within parentheses.

ARREST RECORDS
AUTHENTICATE
BIOMETRICS
CAPTURE METHOD
CJIS
CLARKSBURG
COLLECTION
CRIMINAL HISTORY
ELECTRONIC REPOSITORY
EVIDENCE
EXPEDITIOUS
FRICTION RIDGES
HIGH-TECH HUB
IAFIS
IDENTIFICATION
IDENTIFICATION DIVISION
IMPRESSIONS
INKING PLATE
LATENT FINGERPRINTS
LEGIBLE
LIVE SCAN
MASTER FILE
MODALITY
NGI (Next Generation Identification)
PALM PRINTS
POSITIVE IDENTIFICATION
RECORDS MATCH
SCANNER
SEARCH CAPABILITIES
SKIN MARKINGS
STATE-OF-THE-ART
TATTOOS
WEST VIRGINIA

#54 FINGERPRINT IDENTIFICATION

L G Y P B A S G D D W E S T V I R G I N I A Z S Y

I E Q J C V Y K P O L L T Z X Q P W S G R Z N U S

D R Z P O Z S Z I J H E L B I G E L X P N O P B D

E K B L T C O E I N P T E A U X Z G M I I A A U R

N M E F H O E L G X M G E F B U C V O S V X L H O

T O X S I B I H X D L A X M M H K C V M Z U M H C

I D P T Z D I I C J I S R C E Q R J R H Z M P C E

F A E A A G E O G T Q R E K O R M X N N M A R E R

I L D T U I M N M R A C N V I B U C X O X S I T T

C I I E T C K N T E U M X O I N X T M I Y T N H S

A T T O H O X M F I T B S S I D G S P M E E T G E

T Y I F E L F A O X F R S D C T E S H A X R S I R

I K O T N L P T W P N I I K R A C N X S C F X H R

O L U H T E N T G V U S C C R O K I C N X I R Q A

N Z S E I C S V V A I D H A S A C B R E M L E V S

D H Z A C T A Y D F A W V Y T A L E T F H E H E N

I S Y R A I J G A D K E P H K I X C R Y A P J T O

V W F T T O T I P F T G X Q S O O T T A T J Q C I

I T P G E N K O Q I F Y V I N K I N G P L A T E S

S Y R O T S I H L A N I M I R C J T R R S P A F S

I A H M E S T N I R P R E G N I F T N E T A L E E

O N N Y R O T I S O P E R C I N O R T C E L E R R

N Z Y S S E A R C H C A P A B I L I T I E S L P P

U T B W R S C A N N E R E L I V E S C A N M J K M

P O S I T I V E I D E N T I F I C A T I O N H D I

#55 FBI DIRECTORS AND ACTING DIRECTORS

Since its beginning in 1908, the FBI has been led by a single individual. At first called "Chief," this leader has been titled "Director" since 1919. The FBI Director is appointed by the President of the United States for a single term of no longer than 10 years, is confirmed by the Senate, and answers directly to the attorney general.

Locate and redact or circle the following words within the grid. The words may be hidden horizontally, vertically, or diagonally and may appear backward or forward. Ignore words contained within parentheses.

ALEXANDER BIELASKI

ANDREW MCCABE (ACTING)

CHRISTOPHER WRAY

CLARENCE KELLEY

FLOYD CLARKE (ACTING)

JAMES ADAMS (ACTING)

JAMES COMEY

J. EDGAR HOOVER

JOHN OTTO (ACTING)

LOUIS FREEH

L. PATRICK GRAY (ACTING)

ROBERT MUELLER

STANLEY FINCH

THOMAS PICKARD (ACTING)

WILLIAM ALLEN (ACTING)

WILLIAM BURNS

WILLIAM FLYNN

WILLIAM RUCKELSHAUS (ACTING)

WILLIAM SESSIONS

WILLIAM WEBSTER

#55

FBI DIRECTORS AND ACTING DIRECTORS

G W I L L I A M R U C K E L S H A U S U J Y J J L
H P O F G G T D I F N T R I Y H Z D U X W V O Y O
U T T P L F G U K V K P H J C E F S H D V H H J U
M B T G C O O V H D A L W N D K M N M V V Q N B I
N J W Y H J Y C E J Z E U W I R B O P M M T O A S
N D I B R J Y D Q J K N B E K Y Q I C K M M T U F
R R L T I Z N W C R Q B E W S D J S E S U U T Y R
E A L Q S Y S I U L H P R P A R S S P Z E O O C E
L K I F T A O L K J A F G V L E M E Y B J M L X E
L C A N O V H L E Q T R D N E V A S X P E H A W H
E I M D P D H I Y S C Z K Y I O W M P Z V C O J O
U P W C H E Z A Q K W R E E B O U A L L J N V Y R
M S E A E Q U M F I D S F A R H J I H L Y I Q G I
T A B J R B F B B J A G E I E R E L Z J W F W M I
R M S G W A H U V Y E P G K D A K L Y Z H Y I D K
E O T T R N N R C C H Q X H N G Z I K Q W E L D D
B H E I A I N N A A K R V H A D E W T V U L L R K
O T R B Y Z B S Y L L V T K X E B Q D Z W N I O O
R Y A R G K C I R T A P L T E J C G B P L A A G C
Z B A N D R E W M C C A B E L S G Y J M W T M F W
X K O X R R M P D Z K H S Y A T P Z S N P S A V Q
T Z Z W I L L I A M F L Y N N K T P V A P U L Y C
Z D Z V K P P A H G R S I T M I J T I P B G L R P
S M A D A S E M A J Y H Y W U C K Q I Q Z Q E Q E
I Y A U J C L A R E N C E K E L L E Y M H H N B A

#56 INFAMOUS BAD GUYS

In 1908, when the FBI was first established, agents investigated mostly white-collar and civil rights cases, including antitrust, land fraud, banking fraud, naturalization and copyright violations, and peonage (forced labor). However, as new federal laws were enacted, the FBI's law enforcement responsibilities increased. Catching early-day gangsters, spies, murderers, and crooks, helped shape the FBI's law enforcement reputation and expertise for serving and protecting the American people.

Locate and redact or circle the following words within the grid. The words may be hidden horizontally, vertically, or diagonally and may appear backward or forward. Ignore words contained within parentheses.

AL CAPONE	D. B. COOPER	LUCKY LUCIANO
ALGER HISS	ETHEL ROSENBERG	MA BARKER
ALVIN "CREEPY" KARPIS	FRANK "JELLY" NASH	"MACHINE GUN" KELLY
"BABY FACE" NELSON	FRITZ DUQUESNE	"PRETTY BOY" FLOYD
BARKER BROTHERS	JAMES EARL RAY	ROGER TOUHY
BONNIE PARKER	JOHN DILLINGER	SIRHAN SIRHAN
BRUNO HAUPTMANN	JULIUS ROSENBERG	VELVALEE DICKINSON
CLYDE BARROW	LEE HARVEY OSWALD	WILLIAM HALE

#56

INFAMOUS BAD GUYS

K N V Q G R E B N E S O R S U I L U J V U Z R S B
Z N P R T R I E F R I T Z D U Q U E S N E Y L L R
M O A G W U D B C O O P E R Q R O Y N Y Y U L C O
T B N O S L E N E C A F Y B A B I R D X A N P Q Z
Y F V N A H R I S N A H R I S B I L T B H O P P Y
F A A M A A R S R Y G F P E I K D Z I Q A S Q F U
R L T X E N F T E E M Z V W P H R R X Z Y N Y B S
A F X X H T T Q H O Y T B K R D J P T D V I D N F
C S P J O W I R T T B R R H A Y T Z L N A K H F M
A N X A C M Y C O Y U D U M K O E N O P A C L A F
C L Y D E B A R R O W V N A Y L K V Q H P I Y N R
E E J L K B W N B G L Q O C P F K D R E R D A F A
T E J C O X B F R O U P H H E Y H B E L O E R R N
H H O X G T Z X E W W X A I E O I E K A G E L E K
E A H X M X U B K Y R K U N R B T Q R H E L R K J
L R N V A O Y S R R P X P E C Y J Q A M R A A R E
R V D B M L A G A H N D T G N T I X P A T V E A L
O E I P K P G S B B Y I M U I T Q Q E I O L S B L
S Y L D Z G X E K V R G A N V E J H I L U E E A Y
E O L A H I Y N R H G S N K L R W G N L H V M M N
N S I P G X P T U H J A N E A P D M N I Y Z A K A
B W N A Y U J K E B I E O L B D V I O W P H J L S
E A G C L U G L J B W S B L Q D Q M B Q D X I P H
R L E G K D D W C Q S R S Y O C B H D M X Y R S S
G D R Z R X Y I T A L U C K Y L U C I A N O L S X

#57

UNDERCOVER AGENTS

The use of an undercover agent (UCA) is considered only after other covert investigative methods and tools--such as the use of informants, consensual monitoring, and electronic surveillance--have been explored. Before an undercover agent can be introduced into an investigation, authorization from FBI Headquarters (FBIHQ) must be obtained. The case agent interviews the potential UCAs about the assignment and selects the agent determined to be the best fit.

Locate and redact or circle the following words within the grid. The words may be hidden horizontally, vertically, or diagonally and may appear backward or forward. Ignore words contained within parentheses.

ASSIGNMENT
BACKSTOPPING
BODY RECORDER
CAMEO
CASE AGENT
CONTACT AGENT
COVERT
DANGEROUS
DEEP COVER
DIGITAL RECORDER
EXTRACTION
FALSE IDENTITY
GROUP I
HIGH STAKES
IMPERSONATION
IMPROVISE
INFILTRATE
ISOLATED
LONG TERM
MANIPULATORS
NEGOTIATORS
OFF-SITE
PSYCHOLOGICAL SUPPORT
SAFETY CONCERNS
SCENARIO
SECRET LIFE
SENSITIVE
SHORT TERM
SHOW MONEY
SPECIALTY TRANSFER
STING OPERATION
SUITABILITY
UCA
UC COORDINATOR
UCO (Undercover Operation)
UNDERCOVER SCHOOL
WISEGUY

#57

UNDERCOVER AGENTS

U Y G C J R S H O W M O N E Y F C O V E R T I B V
I F R G N I P P O T S K C A B B D P C L L K E L S
J Y O M Y U C A R E D R O C E R Y D O B O G F U G
T N U I N D R O O S A W T Q I T C Q E W W D I Q D
R R P F D C E D E W Y T I L I B A T I U S L L D U
O K   K C O N V C M N O I T A R E P O G N I T S K
P S I P W B P R T D A Z H I I C S C E C V C E J B
P M P K W S U N D E R C O V E R S C H O O L R P E
U S Z E F Y U Q O I R A N E C S N C J U L N C T T
S B C N C I J O Y F W N D I M P R O V I S E E B A
L C I S F I S Z R S L L A R E V O C P E E D S Y R
A U U F R S A O R E D R O C E R L A T I G I D Y T
C A C L W O E L L S G T N E M N G I S S A S W T L
I C O C S O T K T A E N E I T F Y I G O T M I I I
G N A L O R A A A Y T N A T O A C G O I N R S T F
O O M S M O O R L T T E S D W W S Q V R E E E N N
L I F Y E R R T T U S R D I N I S P F V G T G E I
O T U F U A E D A X P H A C T H E T W T A T U D U
H C Y Z S W G T I I L I G N X I R Q R Z T R Y I F
C A V R M I S E G N T Y N I S O V Z O S C O G E S
Y R L N S F T I N N A O J A H F L E B H A H X S A
S T D Y R V U E N T O T G W M W E R B Q T S A L A
P X C H E D S F E D N L O E B N L R D F N O I A F
Q E S A F E T Y C O N C E R N S R H U O O N B F C
T N O I T A N O S R E P M I M R W O R U C N S C B

#58 HUMAN INTELLIGENCE

The FBI relies heavily on human intelligence (HUMINT), also referred to as informants, cooperating witnesses, confidential sources, and assets, to collect information not accessible by other means. Guidelines have been established to set standards for human source development, validation, evaluation, targeting and exploitation, and to ensure these standards are met.

Locate and redact or circle the following words within the grid. The words may be hidden horizontally, vertically, or diagonally and may appear backward or forward. Ignore words contained within parentheses.

ASSETS

CHS (Confidential Human Source)

COMPLIANCE

CONCERNED CITIZEN

CONFIDENTIAL

COOPERATING WITNESS

COORDINATOR

DECEPTION

EVALUATION

FIRST-HAND KNOWLEDGE

GUIDELINES

HANDLER

HUMINT (Human Intelligence)

IDENTIFY

INFORMANTS

INFORMER

INTRUSIVE

KEEP TABS

MANIPULATORS

MISSION CRUCIAL

MOTIVATION

NEGOTIATORS

OVERSIGHT

PLEA DEAL

PRIVILEGED INFORMATION

RECRUIT

SENSITIVE

SNITCH

SOURCE

SOURCE DEVELOPMENT

STREET SMART

TARGET

VALIDATION

WHISTLEBLOWER

WITSEC (Witness Security Program)

#58

HUMAN INTELLIGENCE

H T K M A N I P U L A T O R S S I J A E S T Y F Q
N M C W M T X E O W T G E U X H W F N E A H Q G I
I C Z Q G R O T K C J H M F Q A W I B F U K C Z E
I N N M T C H T N O I T P E C E D R F U E R P Z G
D L H S D U E U E M D Q M Z D E I S D H V E R N K
E A U E B F N S I G Z K L Y V I Y T L C C M I N S
N E M N U Y G N T Q R Y J I A I L H W T N R V E S
T D I I S K S V G I R A T A S N A A B I R O I G E
I A N L A C S M F O W I T U T E F N L N V F L O N
F E T E A S B W O S S Q S F N Z L D N S B N E T T
Y L Q D I Z S P O N S Q R R E I X K S S C I G I I
S P G I D U D E E S V F L D M T A N T B N R E A W
V W S U O D C S T Q Y V A C P I H O R N Z B D T G
A H T G U T W Q W S E I I O O C N W E T X I I O N
L I N Y T E I C P V O N C N L D M L E Q C H N R I
I S A H I S N O Y P H T U F E E M E T M O A F S T
D T M O U B O M X A O R R I V N O D S O O N O B A
A L R V R A I P S C L U C D E R P G M T R D R S R
T E O E C T T L E J B S N E D E G E A I D L M B E
I B F R E P A I Y E B I O N E C Q G R V I E A D P
O L N S R E U A F C S V I T C N J V T A N R T N O
N O I I U E L N K R J E S I R O R F B T A L I N O
H W Z G Q K A C I U P M S A U C A V W I T J O L C
D E F H U I V E K O R F I L O H I D H O O F N Q S
B R G T I S E T J S R S M W S T H L Q N R L E F H

#59 VIOLENT GANGS

The FBI is dedicated to disrupting and dismantling the most significant gangs through intelligence-driven investigations and initiatives and partnerships, such as Safe Streets Task Forces, the National Gang Intelligence Center (NGIC), and Transnational Anti-Gang Task Forces.

Locate and redact or circle the following words within the grid. The words may be hidden horizontally, vertically, or diagonally and may appear backward or forward. Ignore words contained within parentheses.

AFFILIATION
ANTI-GANG INITIATIVES
BANDIDOS
BLACK DISCIPLES
BLACK MAFIA
BLOODS
CRIPS
DISMANTLE
DISRUPT
DIXIE MAFIA
DOMINICAN GANGS
DRUGS
GANGSTER DISCIPLES
HELLS ANGELS
JAMAICAN POSSES
KING COBRAS
LATIN KINGS
MARA SALVATRUCHA
MEXICAN MAFIA
MOTORCYCLE GANGS
MULTIPLE HOMICIDE
NGIC
OUTLAWS
PAGANS
SAFE STREETS TASK FORCE
SKINHEADS
SMUGGLING
STREET GANGS
TAG (Transnational Anti-Gang)
TATTOOS
TURF WARS
VICE LORDS

#59

VIOLENT GANGS

C U J I A H C U R T A V L A S A R A M N Y H Q S S
S U V M E X I C A N M A F I A M I F O Q Y E Y A G
S V J H O K L B G N I L G G U M S I C U F L S F N
O O X D W S T R E E T G A N G S T A H S D L E E A
V W D A U E W F P E R B B S I A S N D W I S S S G
B O J I F J N J F A L A S P I S E T M C X A S T E
J T P X D O U M I Q G E U L Y W L I U E I N O R L
E C X J J N I T R I M A I I T A P G L R E G P E C
L Y E D B M A R P T M F N H C L I A T U M E N E Y
T Y L I D L E B O Q F N L S K T C N I P A L A T C
N H E S K M O V B A C S Y X T U S G P D F S C S R
A X L R V G P O P A R I A K H O I I L O I Q I T O
M C I U Y X G E D F B V G B X E D N E M A J A A T
S B T P U S Z S V S O B N N K I R I H I X M M S O
I S L T Q W A S D O Y Q W K A T E T O N H Q A K M
D G C A B N P R Y R U O T W A Y T I M I W N J F R
X N W U C I A W B M O J U T G T S A I C L L H O S
K I P G R K K Y Q O X L T W T R G T C A T M X R D
T K N C U N M J B Y C O E Y Z S N I I N D P A C A
X N Q N J J Q A B R O G K C Y M A V D G L Z F E E
Q I V D F B O Y F S T W N Z I T G E E A J K N S H
I T L X T C U Y S I G I J I H V C S K N G J G O N
I A S R A W F R U T A B K V K H D V N G C U B B I
E L U O G Q B L A C K D I S C I P L E S R Z G O K
I Y A J R B M K M U X Z D S J H R R Z D O F E P S

#60 DRUG TRAFFICKING

The FBI has determined that the most effective means of combating drug trafficking is to use the enterprise theory of investigation, which focuses investigations and prosecutions on entire criminal enterprises rather than on individuals. The theory supports not only the prosecution of the criminal enterprise, but also the seizure of the enterprise's assets. It is intended to disrupt or dismantle entire criminal organizations.

Locate and redact or circle the following words within the grid. The words may be hidden horizontally, vertically, or diagonally and may appear backward or forward. Ignore words contained within parentheses.

ASSET SEIZURE
CARTELS
CASH-ONLY
COCAINE
CONTRABAND
CONTROLLED BUY
CRACK
CRIMINAL ENTERPRISE
DEA (Drug Enforcement Administration)
DISMANTLE
DISRUPT
DISTRIBUTION

DRUG DOGS
DRUG LORDS
DRUG MULE
ECSTASY
EL CHAPO
ENTERPRISE
FENTANYL
HEROIN
HIDDEN COMPARTMENT
ILLEGAL DRUGS
JOINTS
MARIJUANA

METHAMPHETAMINE
MONEY LAUNDERING
NARCOTICS
PILLS
RICO (Racketeer Influenced and Corrupt Organizations)
SINALOA CARTEL
SMUGGLING
SYNDICATE
TABLETS
TRAFFICKING
TUNNELS
VIOLENCE

#60

DRUG TRAFFICKING

U J B T E S I R P R E T N E D M S T N I O J R C E
E P N R C C G C U V Y A Y N B E F H C C U P R J N
T H P A F E S P B E H U W D C E Q T I R Y O E E I
A I Y F N S J S U O Q U B S C I T O C R A N N M M
C D S F J I S O M M D B T D W X X A Y Z F C N Q A
I D Q I J R E S F E A A D R E C X W B I R I K V T
D E L C Q P L D B V S O R O M L K Q E H O F W R E
N N Y K H R U R H Y S X O K M D L Y H R P D E A H
Y C N I N E M O I T E J B H V R K O E D M G F V P
S O A N O T G L C A T M H S K S G H R Z S F X Y M
G M T G I N U G A B S U Q G Z P M X E T I R S U A
G P N F T E R U H L E N F U O I E Y C T N D T Q H
L A E M U L D R E E I K H R A L N G A T A O X Y T
C R F R B A J D D T Z B M D F L I N S S L X C F E
H T O N I N B V H S U Z W L N S A I H R O B L U M
F M P O R I C O N T R A B A N D C L O I A L O F A
X E K U T M T R O P E V D G M S O G N J C F R V N
V N X M S I C X P K J D H E D G C G L F A X I I A
Q T X T I R E O A M E U E L S H W U Y U R U C O U
J G L P D C W J H U I V Q L W T N M Q X T C O L J
K X U U E O W B C S Q P A I O P B S D Q E P H E I
D B C R R L T M L X E L T N A M S I D C L A A N R
L B V S H R S L E N N U T T S G O D G U R D V C A
N S G I X I M O N E Y L A U N D E R I N G O U E M
H J G D S U C A R T E L S N G E F N W Z S L A S R

#61 BANK ROBBERY

In 1934, it became a federal crime to rob any national bank or state member bank of the Federal Reserve System. Jurisdiction was delegated to the FBI. Each year, bank robbers collectively steal millions of dollars from banks, credit unions, savings and loan associations, armored car companies, and related businesses. In some cases, these criminals have weapons, and often threaten, and sometimes kill, employees and customers.

Locate and redact or circle the following words within the grid. The words may be hidden horizontally, vertically, or diagonally and may appear backward or forward. Ignore words contained within parentheses.

ARMORED CAR
BAIT MONEY
BANK MANAGER
BANKNOTE
BANK TELLER
CASHIER
DEMAND NOTE
DESCRIPTION
DISGUISE
DYE PACK
FDIC (Federal Deposit Insurance Corporation)
FEDERALLY INSURED
GETAWAY CAR
GPS TRACKER
HEIST
LATENT FINGERPRINTS
LOOT
MARKED BILLS
MODUS OPERANDI
NEIGHBORHOOD CANVASS
PHOTO SPREAD
SERIAL NUMBERS
SILENT ALARM
SUNGLASSES
SURVEILLANCE CAMERAS
SWITCH VEHICLE
TAKEOVER ROBBERY
TIPSTER
UNSUB (Unknown Subject)
VICTIM CUSTOMERS

#61

BANK ROBBERY

T M C A N L A T E N T F I N G E R P R I N T S X P
A S B C B E H J F G P B A N K N O T E E T L M W L
R Z D E S C R I P T I O N A F F S M F P C L E X M
Z T I E A F G S D F E D E R A L L Y I N S U R E D
X W S U R V E I L L A N C E C A M E R A S J L K H
R C G Q R J N W J U Z O X C A S H I E R L C V F I
U Q L K H M R E Y W P H O T O S P R E A D C S S J
V G C X X Z F E N F C L X Z J A Q J H B B Q S L B
R T W H V D U Z M E L C I H E V H C T I W S A L D
K R T Z I Y T S R E M O T S U C M I T C I V V I E
M S Z C N R C R R E S I U G S I D C R F N L N B M
X L E B V R E U B S T P I B Y Q E S K O S M A D A
S M U R D R Z K K H D J T Z K E U Z Z Z O O C E N
B R R I I W A X C I X D R T W N N S H D E D D K D
D A Y E X A X C H A Y D J Z G L K O U M M E O R N
T L N X L M L Y Y E R U Q L T U P S M U T A O A O
I A U K H L B N P A Q T A B Z X O L R T R F H M T
P T E Z M L E A U V W S S C D P W P A M I D R Y E
S N K K E A C T A M S A F P E U B B O N K A O N J
T E E B D K N Q K E B F T R G M I R A N Y U B H A
E L Y A U D S A S N N E A E X E E P R V K W H W Q
R I V E V S J D G V A N R Q G D T S I E H Q G G R
L S X J H A N P Z E D B P S C D E B E R J O I Q F
Y R T O O L J U T I R U J A W M V S P Q L J E H U
L H P N T A K E O V E R R O B B E R Y X O B N V U

#62

HALL OF HONOR - 1

The FBI honors its men and women who have made the ultimate sacrifice in service to their country. To date, 36 Special Agents whose deaths were the direct result of the actions of an adversary have received the designation of Service Martyr. These agents are memorialized at FBI Headquarters and in field offices so that their ultimate sacrifice will always be remembered.

Locate and redact or circle the following words within the grid. The words may be hidden horizontally, vertically, or diagonally and may appear backward or forward. Ignore words contained within parentheses.

BARRY LEE BUSH	JOHN L. BAILEY	SAMUEL P. COWLEY
BENJAMIN P. GROGAN	JOSEPH J. BROCK	SAMUEL S. HICKS
CHARLES W. ELMORE	L. DOUGLAS ABRAM	TERRY R. ANDERSON
HERMAN E. HOLLIS	LEONARD W. HATTON	W. CARTER BAUM
JACK R. COLER	RAYMOND J. CAFFREY	WILLIAM H. CHRISTIAN, JR.
JERRY DOVE	ROBIN L. AHRENS	WIMBERLY W. BAKER

#62

HALL OF HONOR – 1

```
Z X S G S N M J C N E R O M L E W S E L R A H C X
L Z Y P B I M U S A F Z P Q T T H N D F H S L J L
P H S Z E U N M G Z R T J S A M U E L S H I C K S
L I N H N Y E L I A B L N H O J A Z O K A S A H C
M Y E F J Y F W G E A P N Z A M A F N Z Z Y W K J
I Z R B A G D G S I K Q L H E N V H O A D K O O I
V V H A M H Z R N O E M T A I F C Q H G S C S P N
W Q A R I Z C S A W Y E X Z Y W N E I B M E E Y D
T E L R N D X J W Y K M Y Y K E R B L V P X N X N
R S N Y P W T P E D M O U J G M N E V H E V X O B
D R I L G C U Y W R I O S A A S O C J S T X S O A
W E B E R D A J Q J R Q N N B N I B Q K J R A F Y
V K O E O W K B A F D Y E D A R R B I A E Y B Z E
R A R B G O Y C Z T B H D R J O E V F D Z I J J L
U B V U A E K G T N O R D O C C L T N X Q N V I W
B W M S N R P W F L A W Y K V C A A R B R C R I O
X Y J H C N V F L M H M A H K E R F Z A U P N H C
Q L B O A A C I Q A R O G J U Y I L F G C S D C P
O R L K P H S Y T C L B I I R U B Q B R Q W M Q L
M E Z R B O R T F U G M L R D B T O H X E G F X E
R B Z S Z P O Z T I X N E Q I D V U U S L Y A Z U
S M J M R N Q Z X H O T G T S U K P R T A C C U M
J I I H Q E H I G Z V V W G M N N A I P C M U R A
T W X N T G D A S J M A R B A S A L G U O D L Y S
E R J N A I T S I R H C H M A I L L I W J B F B M
```

#63 HALL OF HONOR - 2

The FBI honors its men and women who have made the ultimate sacrifice in service to their country. To date, Special Agents whose deaths were the direct result of the actions of an adversary have received the designation of Service Martyr. These agents are memorialized at FBI Headquarters and in field offices so that their ultimate sacrifice will always be remembered.

Locate and redact or circle the following words within the grid. The words may be hidden horizontally, vertically, or diagonally and may appear backward or forward. Ignore words contained within parentheses.

ANTHONY PALMISANO
CHARLES LEO REED
DOUGLAS M. PRICE
EDWIN C. SHANAHAN
EDWIN R. WOODRIFFE
GREGORY W. SPINELLI
HUBERT J. TREACY, JR.
J. BRADY MURPHY
JOHNNIE L. OLIVER
J. ROBERT PORTER
MARTHA DIXON MARTINEZ
MICHAEL JOHN MILLER
NELSON B. KLEIN
PAUL E. REYNOLDS
RICHARD P. HORAN
RONALD A. WILLIAMS
TRUETT E. ROWE
WILLIAM R. RAMSEY

#63

HALL OF HONOR – 2

M T Y E A P P A U L E R E Y N O L D S I D Q O M L
W P G H S S R P G H U B E R T J T R E A C Y J R N
Z C I H P B D X H X Y E S M A R R M A I L L I W W
E O M D B R O M D S W V A Z J Y G E O Q N J B F X
N G R I E M U O K N Z D L D D H L G N B L E K Z S
I X J X C R G M R G A H G Y S T R V A B A W P X Y
T O X N T H L S Y S J H X W B N A C S F C O K I I
R N J E Z N A G G D D A A L R L H G I K R R E R M
A W B L Z E S E Q N A U U N E U G V M N Q E H E N
M C S S M G M X L L I R Q P A R H R L L P T V T C
N H J O X S P G J J I E B W W H F S A B M T W R F
O A Y N A E R T N Y O K H J A N S K P J M E J O V
X R I B F J I R X Y U H K Y E O P C Y J S U T P H
I L E K S M C J Q H V H N E Y Q R T N Y Z R R T N
D E A L W M E R U Y G E Q M G P Y I O I A T O R H
A S G E D W I N R W O O D R I F F E H G W Q Z E A
H L E I A K C N Z H C Q Z F W L C J T V G D Q B J
T E T N F E A B F I V X B K N S L I N S N W E O V
R O B O H Z Z B A G J B F R S A P E A W W T V R E
A R Y E R I C H A R D P H O R A N T R R C F S J D
M E H X E P M Z F I L L E N I P S W Y R O G E R G
B E C U G D A V V H Q F I K X V L Y S R W X V P W
T D R O N A L D A W I L L I A M S J W Z M X Q F S
R E V I L O L E I N N H O J V O U C N R E D J M B
X W I G L M F W U C I F M Y M U D W J J Z Z Q O I

#64 FUGITIVES

If a local or state police department believes that a person has traveled across a state line or left the country to avoid prosecution or confinement, they may request that the FBI file for an Unlawful Flight to Avoid Prosecution (UFAP) warrant. These warrants are issued by federal judges and allow the Bureau to enter the case and begin a fugitive hunt for the individual at large, using FBI authorized tools and methods to track the target's whereabouts. The fugitive's name and identifying data will also be entered into the National Crime Information Center (NCIC) database.

Locate and redact or circle the following words within the grid. The words may be hidden horizontally, vertically, or diagonally and may appear backward or forward. Ignore words contained within parentheses.

ARMED ROBBERY
ARREST WARRANT
BENCH WARRANT
BOLO (Be on the lookout)
CAPTURED
CASH REWARD
CRIME ALERTS
CRIME BUSTERS
DEPORTATIONS
EXPULSIONS
EXTRADITION
FIREFIGHT
FLYER
FOREIGN EXTRADITIONS
FUGITIVE TASK FORCE
GUN BATTLE
HIDEOUT
JUSTICE
LOCATE
MANHUNT
MEDIA APPEALS
MOST WANTED
MUG SHOT
MURDER SUSPECT
NCIC
POST OFFICE
PUBLIC ASSISTANCE
PUBLICITY
REFUGE
SEX OFFENDERS
SUSPECT
TIPLINE
UFAC (Unlawful Flight to Avoid Confinement)
UFAP (Unlawful Flight to Avoid Prosecution)
US MARSHAL SERVICE
VIOLENT CRIME
WANTED POSTER

#64

FUGITIVES

I L D J R U N H M O S T W A N T E D V R W J S A A
E V Z K E W E E B U R D M R E T S O P D E T N A W
I P H K X D C C J B R R A J P C B B J W U F A C R
O U S T D M I N E B T A N B M S T O H S G U M Y J
K U N F F G V A E R U W H M A C N C K F S I R U S
J L O X I D R T N U O E U Q N N H G B O L E V K F
I K I K R E E S I Z E R N R W D I K S O B Y A H I
O C T E E X S I L C D H T K I U V N Q B D J E Y T
W R I G F T L S P Y I S Z Q X E O R O E Y I C R T
T I D Z I R A S I H H A R I D I V R F C T C R N C
O M A T G A H A T I E C Y E T C D E Q I I F I B E
P E R D H D S C T O E B M A F E F U P F C F M I P
E A T E T I R I U N Q T T V M U Q A V F I E E S S
X L X R S T A L U C A R N R E Y G P N O L Q B L U
P E E U U I M B V E O R A A K C S E I T B V U A S
U R N T S O S U V P A J R S R D I B T S U O S E R
L T G P P N U P E Y V U C A J R F C A O P T T P E
S S I A E T X D Y S D S D X W K A O N P A D E P D
I Z E C C A O G I V B T H J N H T W Y S O G R A R
O G R G T Y Z V S P U I X X G S C O T E Y P S A U
N K O L V I O L E N T C R I M E R N A S A C S I M
S A F S N H S R E D N E F F O X E S E F E I Y D R
G Z Y F B O L O E W W R L P F K K G U B Q R I E C
C M D G U N B A T T L E L C I E T A C O L H R M S
L O F N F U G I T I V E T A S K F O R C E L R A N

#65 KIDNAPPING

Kidnapping is typically charged at the state level because the victim was not taken across state lines. However, the FBI will monitor the situation and offer assistance, including use of the FBI Laboratory. In the case of a missing child, 12 years or younger, the FBI is authorized to initiate a kidnapping investigation even if there is no known interstate aspect.

On the rare occasion that an American is kidnapped and held overseas, an FBI-led network of experienced investigators, negotiators, and foreign liaisons are in place to assist.

Locate and redact or circle the following words within the grid. The words may be hidden horizontally, vertically, or diagonally and may appear backward or forward. Ignore words contained within parentheses.

AT GUNPOINT
BURIED ALIVE
CAPTORS
CHILD ABDUCTION
CO-CONSPIRATORS
DISAPPEARANCE
DROP-OFF AREA
EXTORTION
HANDWRITTEN LETTER
HOSTAGE TAKING
INSTRUCTIONS
INTERSTATE
JURISDICTION
KIDNAPPER
MANHUNT
MISSING PERSONS
MURDER
NEGOTIATOR
OVERSEAS
PARENTAL KIDNAPPING
PRESUMED DEAD
PROOF OF LIFE
PUBLIC APPEALS
RANSOM NOTE
RECOVERY
RESCUE
RESTRAINED
STATE PROSECUTION
TERRORIST FUNDING
TICKING CLOCK
UNDERGROUND BUNKER
UNMARKED BILLS
VICTIM SPECIALISTS
VIOLENT CRIME

#65

KIDNAPPING

G N I D N U F T S I R O R R E T P L P Z F J Q E A
A E C N A R A E P P A S I D T Z A G K G S U H U W
R O T A I T O G E N T R W E F O R V G K T F R D L
C N N V X Z B C C Q E U C S E R E Y M I E M I H E
D H R M A N H U N T I E R C P L N T I D R S S S O
R C H I L D A B D U C T I O N K T L S N V A R T J
E Q N D W V S X R X K I T J T Q A B S A Y E O A D
T P Z U S I F H E O C B P U Y Z L U I P E S T T R
T U H N L C D O D L O E Y R K B K D N P T R A E O
E B I D N T E S R R L M R I U U I P G E O E R P P
L L O E Y I N T U F C I K S L R D G P R N V I R O
N I D R J M I A M J G R P D I I N K E A M O P O F
E C A G B S A G Q L N C B I N E A L R Z O J S S F
T A E R V P R E X J I T V C S D P G S S S L N E A
T P D O U E T T M U K N Z T T A P F O B N Z O C R
I P D U S C S A H I C E L I R L I U N A A D C U E
R E E N R I E K P I I L P O U I N Q S E R X O T A
W A M D O A R I K J T O H N C V G Y C W N I C I V
D L U B T L X N F S S I M Z T E E X T O R T I O N
N S S U P I R G T O J V K I I R E C O V E R Y N B
A U E N A S I Z A T G U N P O I N T G L W T N I T
H R R K C T I I B N O S C R N T D J D S B N E Y O
A G P E U S P I P Z Y V L R S P I P M B K E X E F
W H S R P E T A T S R E T N I Y K E G E X S V Y I
P R O O F O F L I F E U N M A R K E D B I L L S N

#66 MAJOR THEFT

The FBI offers investigative assistance and intelligence on theft groups to law enforcement and private sector partners to create a unified and coordinated approach to this crime threat. The FBI is involved in these types of thefts because these crimes are increasingly committed by organized criminal enterprises or theft groups and usually cross state and even national boundaries.

Locate and redact or circle the following words within the grid. The words may be hidden horizontally, vertically, or diagonally and may appear backward or forward. Ignore words contained within parentheses.

ARMED ROBBERY

ART THEFT

BLACK MARKET

CARGO THEFT

CARJACKING

CLOTHING BOOSTING

COMPUTER SOFTWARE

CONCEALMENT

DIAMOND-SWITCH

FOREIGN SHIPMENTS

HOTSPOTS

INFANT FORMULA

INTERSTATE SHIPMENTS

ITSP (Interstate Transportation of Stolen Property)

JEWELRY AND GEM THEFT

JSA (Jewelers' Security Alliance)

MERCHANDISE

OVER-THE-COUNTER-DRUGS

PIRACY

PROOF OF VALUE

RETAIL STORES

SATG (South American Theft Groups)

SECURITIES

SHOPLIFTING RINGS

SMASH AND GRAB

STATE LINES

STING OPERATION

STOLEN PROPERTY

THIEVES

UCR (Uniform Crime Reporting)

#66

MAJOR THEFT

E Z R E T A I L S T O R E S F J X X S O N W V T N

R W P C K S S V R Q V O U J P L H K A X S G F A H

X N I H I K E P E Z F I G S Z C B K A K N E C C T

S L R Y S S V I P S F Q Y A T N G W U V H H P W O

G P A E P U E A T C I W M I I N O P T T F T R S K

U Z C R M I V N Q I N D W O I I F R O S D E O T U

R R Y M M I N N I L R S N K R E W G L S F K O N Y

D I C Q P E M F K L D U C A H A R L K E N R F E N

R B J Z F U D I A N E A C F H A K N W V R A O M F

E A K J D U D R O N J T T E C C X P J E Y M F P U

T R R O P M N M O R T W A N S Y R W U I K K V I S

N G R T J S A D A B Y F Z T E N G E W H V C A H Q

U D A S T I T C B Q B X O F S M G I M T P A L S D

O N C W D H B I O T V E N R R T L Y K J P L U N D

C A E Z V G E K E H W A R T M S O A Y B M B E G W

E H Q Q S N F F G Q V I O Y F U E P E A P Y L I G

H S K O X Q B Y T U V E I G B C L J S C Q R I E Q

T A A H S W K W O C E N R F A G H A C T N I L R N

R M M P N O I T A R E P O G N I T S F O O O S O W

E S G T A S G N I R G N I T F I L P O H S H C F I

V W Z O S Y Y N V C L O T H I N G B O O S T I N G

O J O R T K A R S T O L E N P R O P E R T Y I M N

G I N T E R S T A T E   S H I P M E N T S P E B Z

C O M P U T E R S O F T W A R E Z U X D E T L L P

V N N X Z M J E W E L R Y A N D G E M T H E F T O

#67

LAW ENFORCEMENT AND PRIVATE SECTOR PARTNERS

Part of the FBI's mission is to provide leadership and criminal justice services to federal, state, municipal, and international agencies and partners. The FBI also has established strategic relationships with local and state governments, private industry, and academia to protect economic and national security.

Locate and redact or circle the following words within the grid. The words may be hidden horizontally, vertically, or diagonally and may appear backward or forward. Ignore words contained within parentheses.

ATF (Bureau of Alcohol, Tobacco, Firearms and Explosives)

CIA (Central Intelligence Agency)

CITIZENS ACADEMY

COMMUNITY OUTREACH

DEA (Drug Enforcement Administration)

DOJ (Department of Justice)

FBIAA (FBI Agents Association)

FUSION CENTERS

HOMELAND SECURITY

ICCC (Internet Crime Complaint Center)

ICE (Immigration and Customs Enforcement)

INFRAGARD

INTERPOL

IRS (Internal Revenue Service)

LEEDA (Law Enforcement Executive Development Association)

LOCAL POLICE

MARSHAL SERVICE

MCEC (Multi-Cultural Engagement Council)

MILITARY CID (Criminal Investigative Division)

MOU (Memorandum of Understanding)

NATIONAL ACADEMY

NEI (National Executive Institute)

NGC (National Gang Center)

NOBLE (National Organization of Black Law Enforcement Executives)

NSA (National Security Agency)

NYPD (New York City Police Department)

POSTAL SERVICE

SECRET SERVICE

STATE POLICE

TSA (Transportation Security Administration)

USAO (US Attorney's Office)

#67

LAW ENFORCEMENT AND PRIVATE SECTOR PARTNERS

Y M N V B T H L S Z Z E U S K B Y I A I H R B Y R
Y L V Z B P E K R B U V J R S I R U V J O O A P Z
H S E C R E T S E R V I C E U S F U E T M C Y I O
O Y T G D A B S T W Z D D X X D N E J L E O B R T
D F Y A D A I R N Q Q R P E W O E V M T L M F G K
X F M H T C L N E O W A S B B D L A U T A M N A U
D Q B L Y L O M C O J G K L C R M D I K N U T S A
E P Z I C A C D N F L A E K C K I O D Q D N P N F
E O V L A E A I O U R R P O U M L U M X S I Y I A
C S W L C A L O I H X F D I T P I I O P E T K A F
I T W U U Y P W S E G N G U I N T T O M C Y M K H
N A R H N C O C U N O I D O C I A R J X U O A B V
A L F H A P L J F Y Y R R Y C B R D T Q R U R R A
O S J S T A I F Y A C P I Y C R Y T G L I T S G M
H E N F K T C I L Y B J D W Z I C L Y I T R H Y M
N R U H Q W E W S T A T E P O L I C E X Y E A Z D
Z V R R E L F R P V O F X S C L D S R J Z A L S Q
J I P T H S R Y W K I N T E R P O L J N U C S E M
H C I T I Z E N S A C A D E M Y J D E K T H E Q V
C E U I S O V R W Y F M Y H O N M O P B Y X R T O
T T L E F S D O Q D I M Y F G A B J U G V A V A S
X Z C N X E W O M R W G L C H R S E X C R P I Z L
G B T Q T N S G R J F X E W O Q V U G I F C C D Q
W T X W E H A D S P G A H Q Y J H L I T W G E Z N
A N D V Q G H L N A T I O N A L A C A D E M Y G W

#68 FBI VOCABULARY - 1

Match the numbered acronyms, buzzwords, and jargon to the correct lettered definition and meaning.

1. 10-7
2. 10-9
3. 137
4. BOLO
5. BUDED
6. COB
7. CYA
8. FNG
9. KMA
10. POV
11. RDO
12. UNSUB

a. ANONYMOUS PERPETRATOR
b. CASE ASSIGNMENT DEADLINE
c. CRIME ALERT
d. DAY OFF DURING THE WORK WEEK
e. ELIGIBLE FOR RETIREMENT
f. END OF THE WORKDAY
g. HUMINT FILE
h. NON-ISSUED CAR
i. PROBATIONARY AGENT
j. REPEAT THAT TRANSMISSION
k. SAFEGUARD FROM REPERCUSSIONS
l. SIGNING OFF

#69 FBI VOCABULARY - 2

Match the numbered acronyms, buzzwords, and jargon to the correct lettered definition and meaning.

1. 302
2. 5X5
3. BACKSTOPPING
4. BEACH TIME
5. BETTY OR BILLY BU
6. BLUE FLAMER
7. CHOIR PRACTICE
8. COVERING A LEAD
9. CW
10. GOON SQUAD
11. T3
12. WAG

a. AN APPROXIMATION
b. CLEAR RADIO TRANSMISSION
c. EXCESSIVELY DEDICATED EMPLOYEE
d. HAPPY HOUR
e. INSPECTION STAFF
f. LEAVING WORK EARLY
g. NARRATIVE REPORT OF INTERVIEW
h. OVERLY AMBITIOUS AGENT OR SUPERVISOR
i. PLUGGING HOLES IN UNDERCOVER IDENTITY
j. SOURCE EXPECTED TO TESTIFY
k. SUSPENSION
l. WIRE TAP

#70 FBI VOCABULARY - 3

Match the numbered acronyms, buzzwords, and jargon to the correct lettered definition and meaning.

1. BOONDOGGLE
2. BU STEED
3. BULKY
4. CI
5. EYE OR EYEBALL
6. FEDERAL FRIDAY
7. FNU LNU
8. MORE ROAST BEEF
9. ON THE DESK
10. POST AND COAST
11. RED BALLED
12. TICKLE THE WIRE

a. ACTIVITY BETWEEN FILE REVIEWS
b. EVIDENCE VAULT
c. ISSUED WORK VEHICLE
d. POINTLESS ACTIVITY WHICH APPEARS TO HAVE VALUE
e. SOURCE NOT EXPECTED TO TESTIFY
f. STIMULATE RECORDED CONVERSATIONS
g. STUCK AT LIGHT OR PULLED OVER DURING SURVEILLANCE
h. SUPERVISOR OR RELIEF FOR THE DAY
i. TAKING ADVANTAGE OF FBI STATUS
j. THURSDAY
k. VISUAL CONTACT
l. UNNAMED PERSON

#71 FBI VOCABULARY - 4

Match the numbered acronyms, buzzwords, and jargon to the correct lettered definition and meaning.

1. 10-20
2. BRICK TIME
3. HOOVER HIGH
4. IN THE WIND
5. KEEPING BOOK
6. MAHOGANY ROW
7. PONY
8. POW
9. RUN IT INTO THE GROUND
10. STAND DOWN
11. TICKLER
12. WHEELS UP

a. FBI HEADQUARTERS
b. FLYING OUT
c. NON-ISSUED GUN
d. LOCATION
e. PURSUE RELENTLESSLY
f. MAINTAIN RECORDS ON ADVERSARY
g. TASK REMINDER
h. SAC OFFICE SPACE
i. SUSPENSION
j. SAMPLE COMMUNICATION
k. STOP ACTIVITY
l. WHEREABOUTS UNKNOWN

ADULT COLORING PAGES

DEPARTMENT OF JUSTICE
FEDERAL BUREAU OF INVESTIGATION
FIDELITY
BRAVERY
INTEGRITY

THE FBI SEAL

FBI AGENTS

EVIDENCE RESPONSE TEAM CRIME SCENE

HOSTAGE RESCUE TEAM

INSPIRATION TREE
YELLOW BRICK ROAD

FIREARMS TRAINING

CYBER CRIME

FBI K9 GERMAN SHEPHERD

ANSWER KEY

1 - WHAT THE FBI INVESTIGATES

```
P S E T K Y G N I K C I F F A R T N A M U H J R R
M N M B F Q B J S R O T A D E R P E N I L N O T X
S O I W E N O I T P U R R O C C I L B U P K Y V X
I I R S M L I V M D U Q J I U Q N G V Q S U C M O
R T C G I I F V T C N G V B E J T N E S A C R S F
O A C N R Z J T P E S J A U C G E E G G E Y I I S
R G I I C H I G P M K N G S N B R N C N I B M R B
R I M P Y T A E J I K U P R E U S V H A O E I O W
E T O P T M I D V R G R M H G I T I C G R R N R A
T S N A R G Y J O C A E H A I D A R I L G C A R L
L E O N E B B B D R L D T T L E T O V A A R L E F
A V C D P H B R K A C R V E L N E N I N N I E T O
N N E I O E C X X L X U Q C E T T M L O I M N C R
O I T K R M L J O L F M E R T I H E R I Z E T I O
I D P Y P I M X F O U L Y I N T E N I T E F E T L
T N L I X R Z U S C G A A M I Y F T G A D C R S O
A U B A W C R X S E I I R E R T T A H N C Q P E C
N O N X M T G R L T T R T S E H J L T S R K R M F
R R X Q D N T V P I I E T U T E V C S N I R I O P
E G E X M E N V F H V S H J N F N R D A M B S D K
T K V W X L Y V R W E S E S U T B I H R E I E U L
N C W O Z O O R A D S E F F O X H M J T K N S A F
I A D R O I S O U K Y P T J C A S E X C W S O I V
S B A Y N V H R D J Y Y R T N U O C N A I D N I W
C R I M E S A G A I N S T C H I L D R E N N O M N
```

2 - CORE VALUES AND FBI SEAL

```
M M G I T E G D E D E L E V E B D L O G P A T K P
N F Z U K P F E S N A C I R E M A T C E T O R P I
U X F P E S S E N I L N A E L C D X X S Y P X C H
P X Y T I R U C E S L A N O I T A N U U V I E Z S
H R E O Q R L F S E G N E L L A H C N N H H N C R
O D C Y S Y D O S Z F J T P V A L O R I T S F Z E
L Z I T Y T Y K W S O C I P I P T U R T G R O Y D
D W T I P I T S H E R F I G U Y H U Y Y N E R K A
T C S N M L I M I U T Z S J F T I O E O E D C M E
H D U G Y E L U T L Y Y R W O Y R M H F R A E B L
E L J I L D I L E A S T O C Q S T K F P T E C W L
C E N D I I B A S V I I N W M R E D Z U S L R R A
O I E R G F A U T A X R O S Y R E V A R B L I O N
N F I O H S T R R D L G H S G P N T D P I A M G O
S E D F T E N E I I E E C E V F S W I O N N I L S
T U X T U P U L P S A T I N V Q T O V S K O N U R
I L N C W I O L E T V N M D S I A B E E R I A E E
T B R E H R C E S I E I E E Q M R R R M S S L G P
U C L P F T C A V N S T D G U I S A S G R S L A W
T Y U S Y S A F U C M X A G T Y S N I B E E A R W
I G I E M D V M R T W Q C U Y Y W C T T M F W U L
O T U R I E P E A I M K A R S X O H Y B A O S O T
N O F U N R S T L O W H T U R T V E C T F R A C G
C O M P A S S I O N D M P S Y B B S N A S P P D U
S O L O L X T T E C A E P D R W F A I R N E S S L
```

3 - FBI JOBS

4 - FBI CORE COMPETENCIES

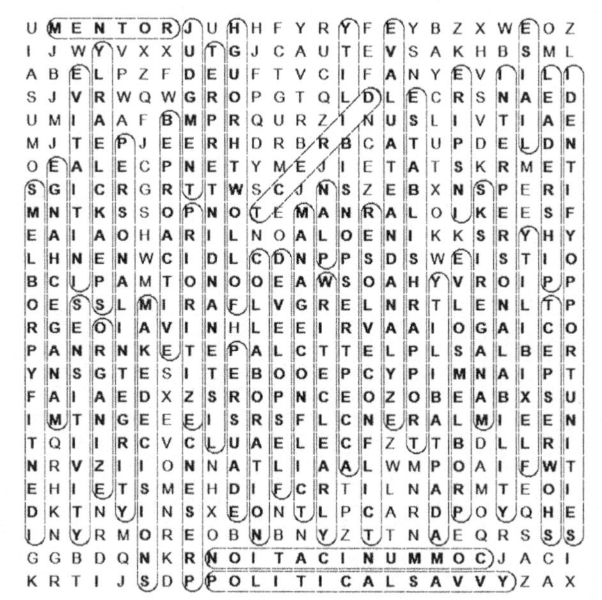

5 - SA QUALIFICATION

```
O H O O V E R R O A D C Q Z H O Q B H P M Q D G L
M P K K Z H C L A S S R O O M I O N B W R C S M E
P R G R A D U A T I O N R M V X J S C X C Y K R G
S X R E E M W K T G U C A K D A O O D P M G C X A
P R Y V E I J D X I M G T U X X R W Q K R O O N L
Q W B W K W B S X U D Z N F D I P M B A Z L V W S
A V C T M L T X N M E Y E I B I L C V B N O E U T
N Z C P L I U I D H K P V Q N O T R R N C H T O U
Y M E D A C A L A N O I T A N I L O R Y O C N F D
S G T V Y H A L L O F H O N O R A N R F U Y E I I
K K D A O R K C I R B W O L L E Y R O I F S M R E
E M W X G R K S C P T A I N Q C X I T N U P N I S
E F I E L D C O U N S E L O R I Q T K S I M G N Y
W Y J V A D E F E N S E T A C T I C S E O J I G S
E T H I C S N V S M O O R M R O D V Y R N Z S R A
N P D R U L W S V J B I M J K N I U U V L M S A P
O W Q W J W Y X X H R D C W T E S Z Z I Z M A N G
Y C A U S D I N I N G H A L L B A C I C A N D G B
T A R R E S T S C E N A R I O S D N I E B N L E L
N S U R V I V A L S K I L L S T A M U M L O E Y V
E B R A N Y B J F J M Q I I U T U Z F M E V I W E
W H S M R A E R I F W P X R O L E P L A Y D F K G
T O Y E L L A S N A G O H B S T E G R A T O A L Z
R E O C I T N A U Q O L N L E Y L M S N S R E C G
I C H A P E L S S E N T I F L A C I S Y H P B H A
```

6 - FBI ACADEMY AND TRAINING

```
S L R S X S B E T Y M L W E C N E I R E P X E O N
E Z E V U G B A C K G R O U N D C H E C K R Z G U
L Y F B C O R E C O M P E T E N C I E S Z E Z W T
E P F S S Y R N H G J E F A W O Q U P Z J V S X L
C D O Y N C T W N P A R R S R I M C A U L I E Z L
T A L G O I E U J U V S E E I T K H N S X A C V H
I R A O I L E S B G A O N T T A H A E Z E W U Q E
O G N E T O R C H Y I N O I T T P R L F A Y R S H
N E O R A P G I Q R L A I S E U A A I J I R I T A
P G I O C R D T E E A L T G N P R C N M K A T N F
R E T C I E N I H S B I A N E E G T T V G T Y E S
O L I S F F A Z C U I N C I X R Y E E A E I C M D
C L D G I S T E A M L T I T A W L R R S V L L E R
E O N N L N E N P E I E L S M A O Q V S I I E R I
S C O I A A E Y W D T G P E B I P K I O T M A I V
S R C S U R M W J Y Y R P T M E V G E C I Y R U E
E Q A S Q T M E F G N I A Q Z T U N W I T X A Q R
R O T A N I D R O O C T N A C I L P P A E D N E S
U P G P I G D D O A Y Y I H C L S D Z T P A C R L
T X K T S E T S S E N T I F W C W K R E M I E C I
N B O Y T I S R E V I D P D Z G E X X S O N Z I C
V A B Z O W X D E E R G E D S R O L E H C A B S E
F I N A N C I A L L Y R E S P O N S I B L E B A N
X W T T T Z T X M T S E T   G U R D K X O V Q B S
N M I E H W H V F M M E D I C A L E X A M B Y X E
```

7 - PHYSICAL FITNESS TEST

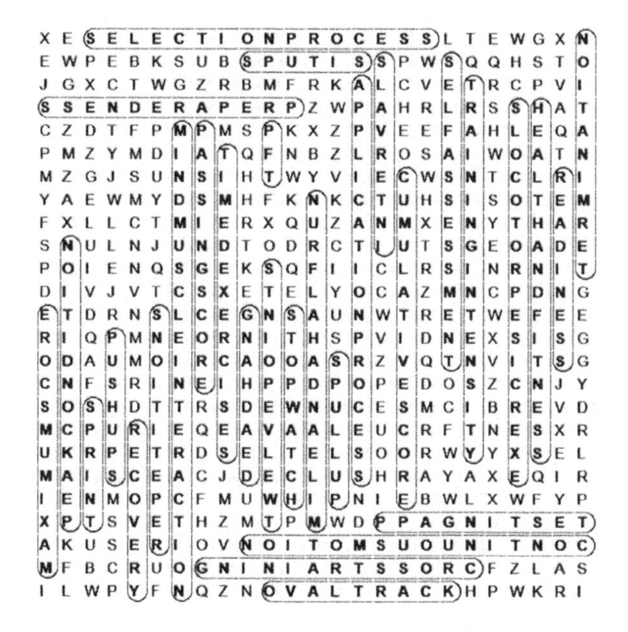

8 - FIELD OFFICES (A THRU L)

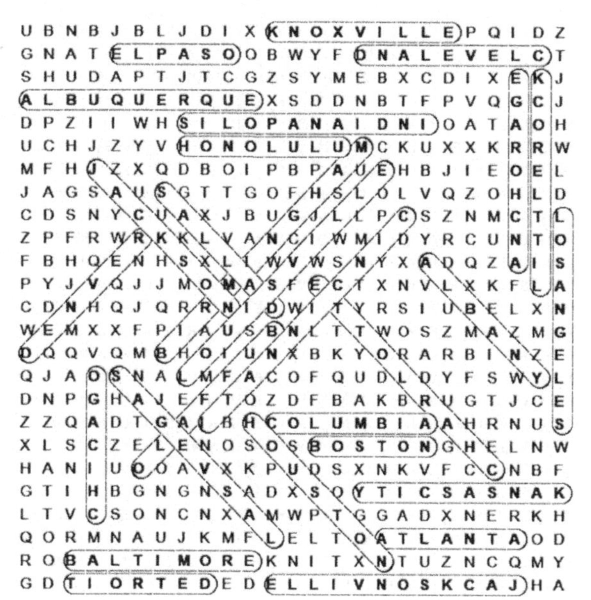

9 - FIELD OFFICES (M THRU Z)

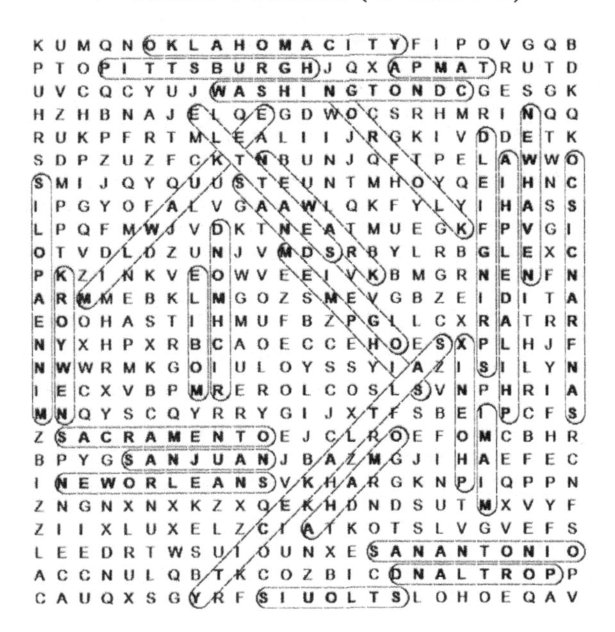

10 - IN THE FIELD OFFICE

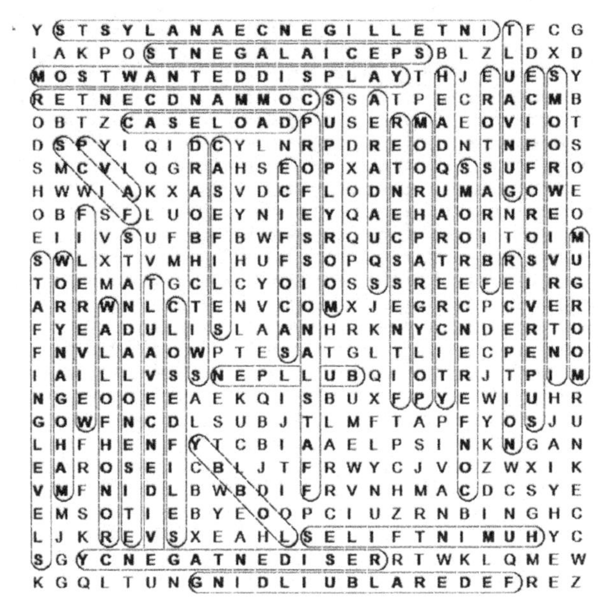

11 - FBI FIELD GEAR

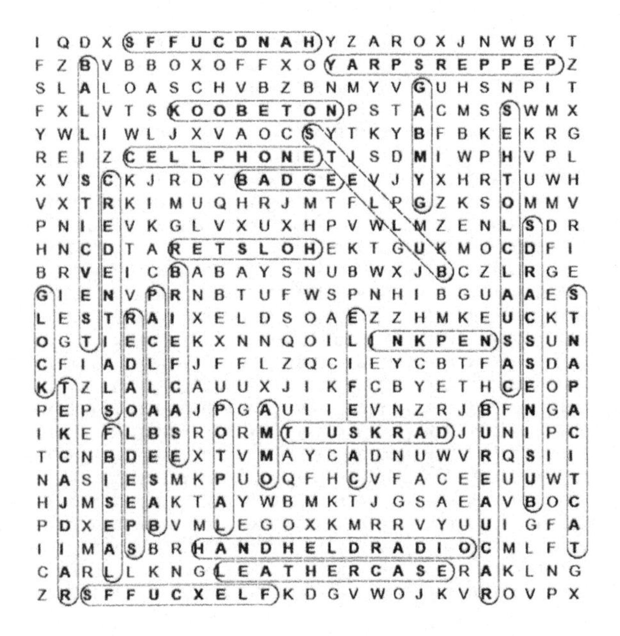

12 - CAREER PATHS & POSITIONS

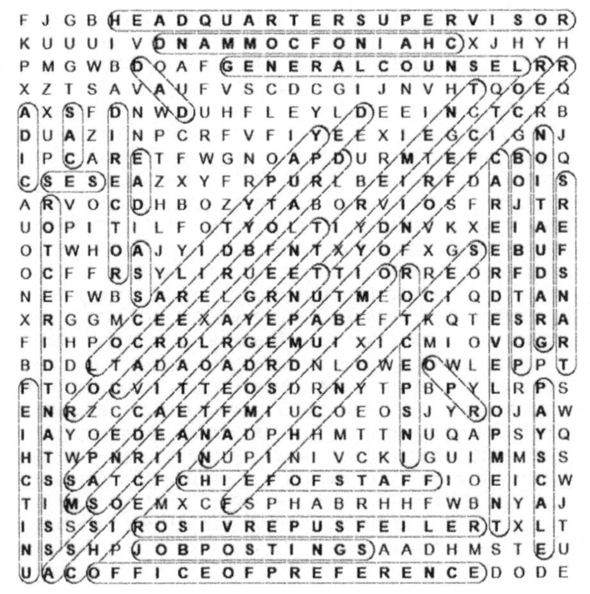

13 - INTERVIEW TECHNIQUES

```
X B G H T Y W E F T Y P I W X N O I T A D I L A V
Y U Y F C V E T P M T E C R E O C X R V U R T Q H
T M L O E S I G Z G N E G O T I A T I O N D C S C
N F O N P E V M E L S D R P U V Q V U D D O E E M
T Q M O S L R F M V D W H F R V R C C S S F J U K
Y N G T E E E K P C R Q Y S Y Q V O T X T D B Q V
R R E Z R B T Q A D I E B P D M L O V Y E S U I C
K K W C X K N K T B W A S Y Q T G P M B R G S N O
H O A Z O L I S H E D I U B U Y R E P G C N H H P
D C T G O N K I I A F E T K O H P R Z O E I C C Z
K B O O O F N W Z V Y G B N J F Q A S O S D I E B
Z S U U K V N I E Z Z Y Q R E F G T E D I N N T P
C O N F E S S I O N S V T C I S V I U C I I T K W
D B S K G H V Z E F E S E Y G E S O C O N F E L I
S M U O H M L C P T G Q Z X I Y F N L P T T R A N
O F G L Q D V I R R A C I P H T C Z A E E C R W F
G P F D A T L L N O U H L C P X F B B T L A O Y O
E U U I Z F U M E P G J A M A S C O R A L F G E R
O O I B X H D C T P N S N P R S G H E V I B A R M
X L V L Q M H B K A A L O S G I M R V I G I T C A
P S N W T C O L E R L K I T Y P A Y N T E V E M N
I P C C R Y S P S O Y V T R L G V N O O N E C T T
L P U Z D A B V D S D Q A E O S B F N M C Q N M S
O B W F J Z Q N X D O S R S P Q H B H C E Q E K D
V I I N H Y Z C X R B I F S S J Y C G P O C D A B
```

14 - ELECTRONIC SURVEILLANCE

```
A S C R E C N E D I V E J V D S P A T E R I W V T
H D A N Y S E C I V E D G N I K C A R T T E S E R
S U R V E I L L A N C E S Q U A D U K S E C E L A
Z P Q Q T N E G A H C E T P Y E S A B A T A D E N
O O O W V P E N R E G I S T E R P R X L A R F C S
T N E M P I U Q E G N I D R O C E R J Y Q T W T M
G R F E T A R T L I F N I L S W V F B S C D S R I
W S U R R E P T I T I O U S E N T R Y B D N R O T
M A U X P D I N F O R M A N T H K H K W B A E N T
H R P S S E N T I W G N I T A R E P O O C P D I E
B C O U R T A U T H O R I Z E D U O I T Y A R C R
N K E X C T U N D E R C O V E R A G E N T R O J N
N O E T W E N O H P O R C I M V W I A O E T C O O
B A I S Z G X B W V N N A L Q I E V N H F T E B I
W X V T W U T R G O N A E R Z D I L M S P N R P T
U I R M A C R D E B G F V B E B N L S E H O L D A
M I H Q G Z O E E D Y F A J E M N V C Q O O A K L
Z I E T P Q I N D Y R N N O S W A R O Q E Z T S L
S E C V R S Q M S R W O Q E V M E C J R D P I R A
C L Q F Q E R K I E O B A J W T C J B P I X G P T
U T S O Z M V I H N N T S S N C Z R U V V I I C S
G I G Y W M C O Q X I S R I I Y O Q I G S J D P N
G T S O B U V S C C J M U U V F X C Q Z P G B T I
V C D T L M D U P K W Z A A O E V I T I S N E S Z
T K L C G G I L O W N Q E O L C H Y R O T I N O M
```

15 - PHYSICAL SURVEILLANCE

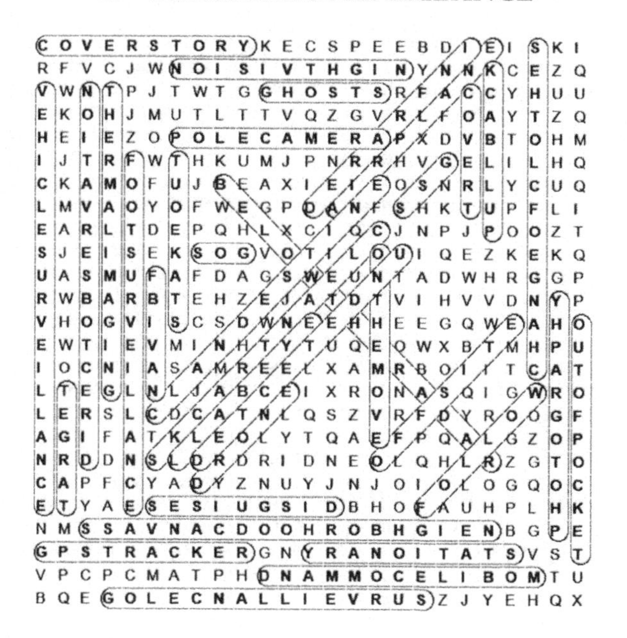

```
C O V E R S T O R Y K E C S P E E B D I E I S K I
R F V C J W N O I S I V T H G I N Y N N K C E Z Q
V W N T P J T W T G G H O S T S R F A C C Y H U U
E K O H J M U T L T T V Q Z G V R L F O A Y T Z Q
H E I E Z O P O L E C A M E R A P X D V B T O H M
I J T R F W T H K U M J P N R R H V G E L I L H Q
C K A M O F U J B E A X I E I E O S N R L Y C U Q
L M V A O Y O F W E G P D A N F S H K T U P F L I
E A R L T D E P Q H L X C I Q C J N P J P O O Z T
S J E I S E K S O G V O T I L O U I Q E Z K E K Q
U A S M U F A F D A G S W E U N T A D W H R G G P
R W B A R B T E H Z E J A T D T V I H V V D N Y P
V H O G V I S C S D W N E E H H E E G Q W E A H O
E W T I E V M I N H T Y T U Q E Q W X B T M H P U
I O C N I A S A M R E E L X A M R B O I I T C A T
L T E G L N L J A B C E I X R O N A S Q I G W R O
L E R S L C D C A T N L Q S Z V R F D Y R O O G F
A G I F A T K L E O L Y T Q A E F P Q A L G Z O P
N R D D N S L D R D R I D N E O L Q H L R Z G T O
C A P F C Y A D Y Z N U Y J N J O I O L O G Q O C
E T Y A E S E S I U G S I D B H O F A U H P L H K
N M S S A V N A C D O O H R O B H G I E N B G P E
G P S T R A C K E R G N Y R A N O I T A T S V S T
V P C P C M A T P H D N A M M O C E L I B O M T U
B Q E G O L E C N A L L I E V R U S Z J Y E H Q X
```

16 - FIREARMS OF THE FBI

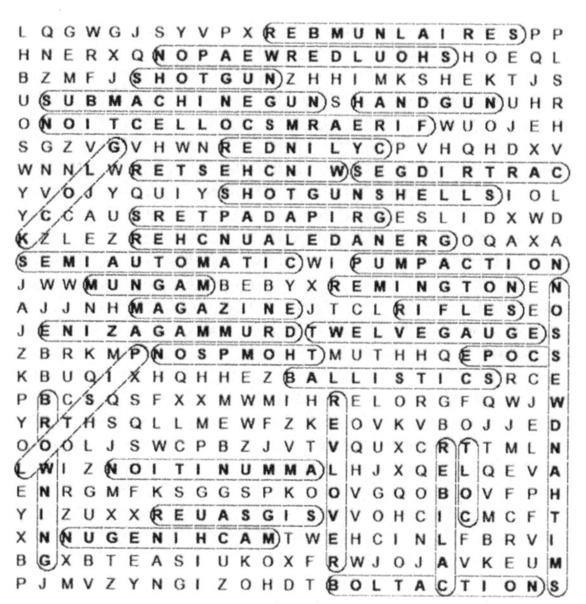

```
L Q G W G J S Y V P X R E B M U N L A I R E S P P
H N E R X Q N O P A E W R E D L U O H S H O E Q L
B Z M F J S H O T G U N Z H H I M K S H E K T J S
U S U B M A C H I N E G U N S H A N D G U N U H R
O N O I T C E L L O C S M R A E R I F W U O J E H
S G Z V G V H W N R E D N I L Y C P V H Q H D X V
W N N L W R E T S E H C N I W S E G D I R T R A C
Y V O J Y Q U I Y S H O T G U N S H E L L S I O L
Y C C A U S R E T P A D A P I R G E S L I D X W D
K Z L E Z R E H C N U A L E D A N E R G O Q A X A
S E M I A U T O M A T I C W I P U M P A C T I O N
J W W M U N G A M B E B Y X R E M I N G T O N E N
A J J N H M A G A Z I N E J T C L R I F L E S E O
J E N I Z A G A M M U R D T W E L V E G A U G E S
Z B R K M P N O S P M O H T M U T H H Q E P O C S
K B U Q I X H Q H H E Z B A L L I S T I C S R C E
P B C S Q S F X X M W M I H R E L O R G F Q W J W
Y R T H S Q L L M E W F Z K E O V K V B O J J E D
O O O L J S W C P B Z J V T V Q U X C R T T M L N
L W I Z N O I T I N U M M A L H J X Q E L Q E V A
E N R G M F K S G G S P K O O V G Q O B O V F P H
Y I Z U X X R E U A S G I S V V O H C I C M C F T
X N N U G E N I H C A M T W E H C I N L F B R V I
B G X B T E A S I U K O X F R W J O J A V K E U M
P J M V Z Y N G I Z O H D T B O L T A C T I O N S
```

17 - FIREAMS TRAINING

A P O S S I B L E C L U B W J K Y A R D L I N E R
J E B M R W C L A Y P I G E O N S U E O S X A Y E
V M I S O S C E L E S P O S I T I O N R W F F T D
C E S Y K Y F R S V I S B I W D F E Z W Q T W R H
M N R F Q Y L I W Z E V A O R R Q E G N A R H R A
G Q O I L S E C I F K A X R D E T R M U G L I C N
P E G S F U L Z U J V W E M B Y T F N X M T M F D
B H U S O T E U H V P B S R J E A O X J I N O S L
N N N W O R H V G H S I T E S M B R O X V J O H E
V E V T P E E G Q S N L W W E Y B R M H L R R O H
D W A Z F Z F J I N P W H R G Y U R W O S M   L Q
P S U F S A G Q R N R Q Q D V V U T Y K R Q G L S
E N L F W E A K H A N D S H O O T I N G R O N O I
T F T U P C O N T R O L T O W E R Y K G F F I W M
F I R I N G L I N E E R I F Y R D U B U O Q N P U
S I M U N I T I O N R O U N D S X E Z T Z U A O L
J O T E G R A T E T T E U O H L I S R F W A E I A
Z T L V M D E A D L Y F O R C E E W H F I L L N T
C A V A I L A B L E C O V E R J H S A R Z I C T O
U L A T S E R V I C E R O U N D C O H K K F N Y R
E P O C S B U F W U K R V Z N O U O T A U Y U Z D
T R I G G E R P U L L T N Y R Z W S R L N O G G E
E E S R U O C L O T S I P E N I V P K M I P M U K
S P E E D L O A D E R B H I C W F O N C W N G M D
Y B U L L S E Y E A M X Z T L I L B J C R P E P A

18 - FBI IN MOVIES

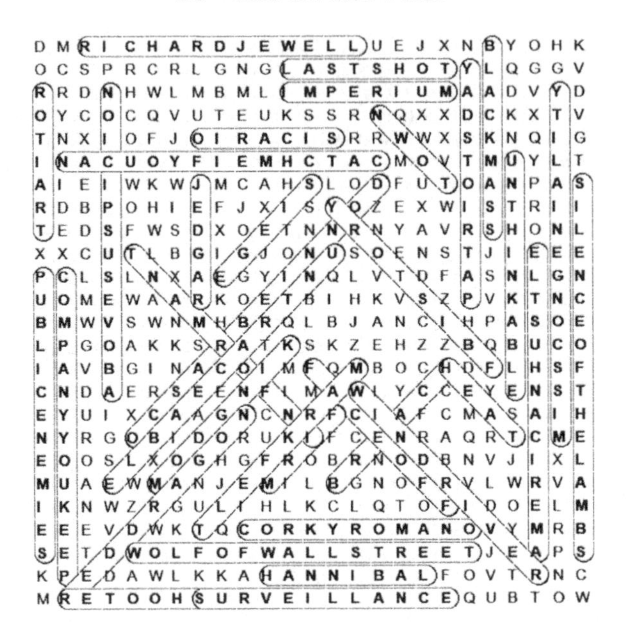

19 - FBI ON TV

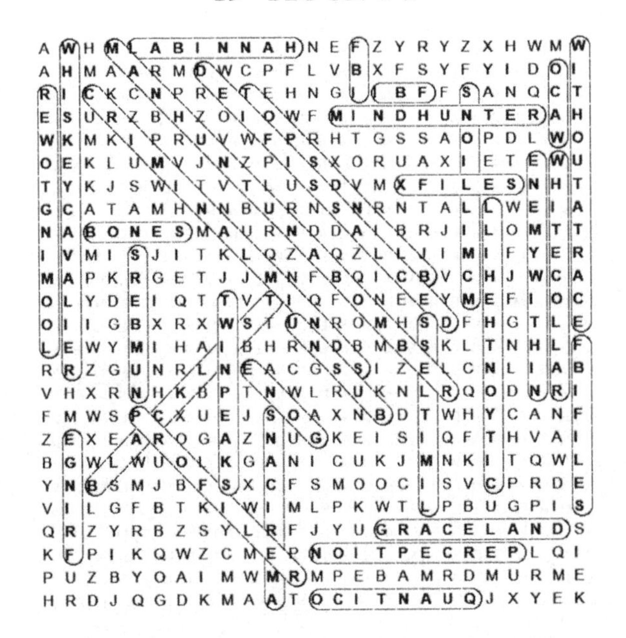

20 - SERIAL MURDER

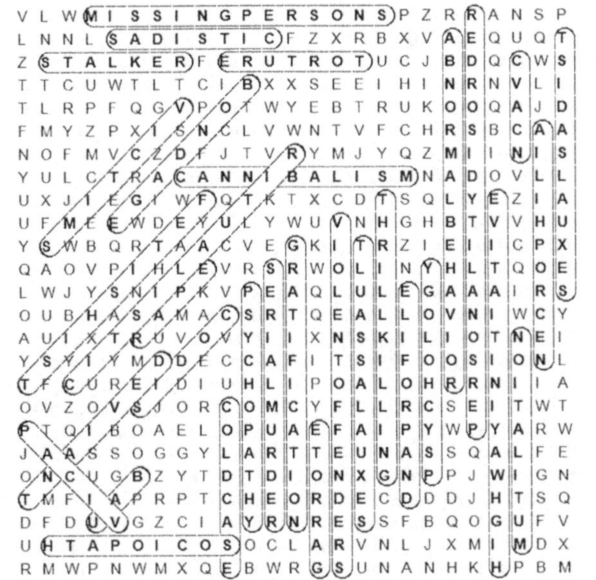

21 - SERIAL KILLERS

K Y W S G C J H R E L G N A R T S N O T S O B W T
R E T S I E M U A B B R E H P L D Z S A B T T V Q
R Y O G K Z G F U T G I J A C K T H E R I P P E R
C O B Y Z I Z H X Q N X L U M Y K J Q G P U J A T
A I L G W E L M C Z N H I P X T A C L V F D U M T
U A V V K T B L E R E L L I K R E V I R N E E R G
N Q N T N I Y R E N A R B L A U Y M D J M M P P D
E Y G R Q W Z N N R O R I G A I H P W U P A E B P
V J P A E K U T N I S S C M Z O H Q R J F S D P K
R G E M R D Q P R I N E E G A I K C V U A F I D T
E E A D F Y A B S E G O R I N R Q H W U F O C O W
R T M R M S R R E J L H B I D S D U Z Z H N I B A
E P R H Y U Q I S D S T T M A Q E R E K F O M T Y
D Z K H A R N N D I L G T S A L B L A T Q S O E N
R T Q J U D A D R G N N O I T I K B R H K M H D E
U L J W S Z Y Y K Q E N J F L A L I W A C I L B W
M V U E J O Z E B E U W E A A L L L L R H I M U I
P W P I Z D U D R Q M W A D K T E K I L L C R N L
F L S P Z I F E S F W P N Y I I R U E W E W T D L
O Y A O K A Y L J Q F L E E I U W C M R M R N Y I
W C K G B C P Z M K D E E R E Z C V Z A E H S R A
Z Q V O H R I O W R A C J S D L K P Q M S R I P M
Y H C W G D A V I D B E R K O W I T Z D U A I D S
M Y C A G E N Y A W N H O J F J P A C X L R F F T
V F G O L D E N S T A T E K I L L E R X Y K H S J

22 - WHITE COLLAR CRIME

O C L M I V O P R E T E N D E R S K G Y A D U U E
O V G M N E X T O R T I O N J Z X U B N X J L Z E
T N T Q Q V B G Z B I V T H I I Q B F U A A M P R
O O F Q L V X E Y H T H P A A D N S T A M A L B D
K L E P T O C R A C Y P L S E W V D R S C I H T E
Z E D W E B L E Q K B X J O O H B S P S Y S C G G
Z C F N L P F S Y B A H I O E T C W C B O D Q N L
O R P B K D E C E P T I O N Z G X L O S F Y I A D
C O R R U P T I O N R R Q V Z Y L Z W C R H G Z U
W Z T W Q D U A R F E T A R O P R O C E S N D J A
R Q G N I R E D N U A L Y E N O M W B I V N U S R
H E A L T H C A R E F R A U D R D I M P S D P S F
J D B E L F A O E E L S P I C N R S Z N B U V K G
Y A P W R J M B V U I G E F U B V H J Q Q A T C N
T Y O K A S E I T I R U C E S K Y Y F F X R G A I
S M L H L S R E C E C O U N T E R F E I T F T B T
E R A M L U I A E K A F J Q X K Z J P L G F R K E
N M U B O Y C D R L B Q R D D O I W W M I P T C K
O N R Q C D A Y X F U M O Z V Q M A U N Y N R I R
H G K I E P N J V R X U I B O M U V C X O B J K A
S V D S T R G W Y N R V M R O N X E J V J I F B M
I G H H I E R A S P O O F I N G N K L L A M B U E
D O L T H W E G N I L A E D F L E S P S N N N J L
C S Z E W O E G G V E T A L U P I N A M D E R K E
M S N V B P D N D H L N N E U S I M P O S T E R T

23 - ECONOMIC CRIME

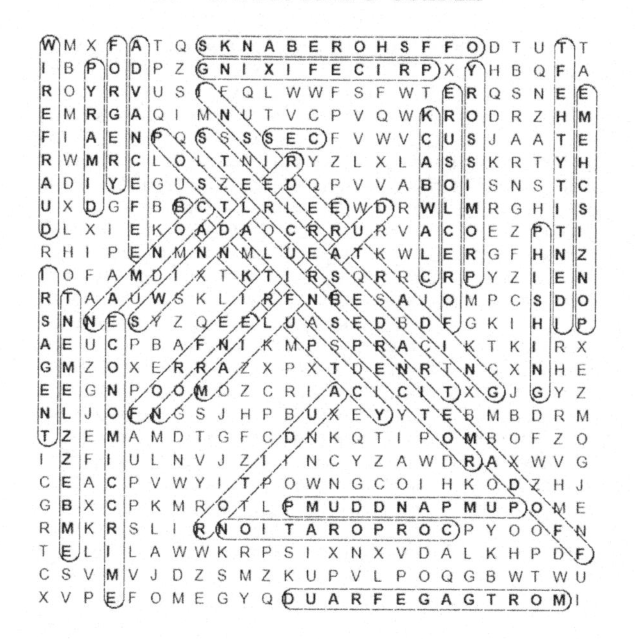

24 - PUBLIC CORRUPTION

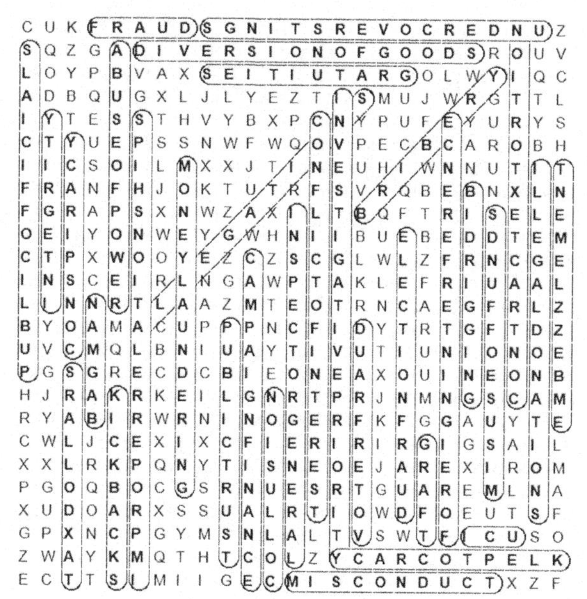

25 - FBI WORKING DOGS

```
A S J M M N J P E D W B I S H O F R A F R T I F V
U X Y D G A B I U D I X D A H O T R E A T I Q R V
A L F G D T N O P B O H N K P F G E S C A L O U W
P P O T R U G J M W I D T S L O H T N R I D B K K
Q I D R U R S H Z B L I S E W K V R O V O S E P W
F W S E G A E M C E S R S C A G T I S B J S D X U
W P A L D L V G R R A N S G E V W E R L S A I H C
V O S A E D I O E L A T I E L N N V E D S R E W A
R M P D T I T D P R W E U F A Q T E P J S S N D D
E X E R E S I Y G T M B S O F H H R G D J U C C A
S E C A C A G P R M U A Z U E I K S N R C H E H V
C C I W T S U A E C G I N O F F N U I X J A T D E
U I A E I T F R N G S N Q S L T O G S O L O R T R
E T L R O E A E T D L U I Q H H L R S Y W S A K D
L C L C N R Y H R J B B O K D E S O I W R X I H O
G A Y O K S W T A I G F S O C W P Y M C D V N I G
S R T C H O G A P R P S O D U A G H K S A T I Z W
I P R F E E O B B U P L Q N R O R E E V F F N S W
P A A P Q G A R N L B Q P Y O E Z T W R B T G X R
S E I D O B T R S G O D G N I K R O W Q D B T R K
D Y N A R C O T I C S D E T E C T I O N D S Z Y B
E Z E D E Z H S Z N N A Q K O B S E R V A T I O N
F R D B I S S C B H G S M E L L O Y F N G Y G D S
K L R O U P A U X U B Y D H U M A N R E M A I N S
T A Q O A L A M I N A E C I V R E S J U G L W X T
```

26 - HOSTAGE RESCUE TEAM

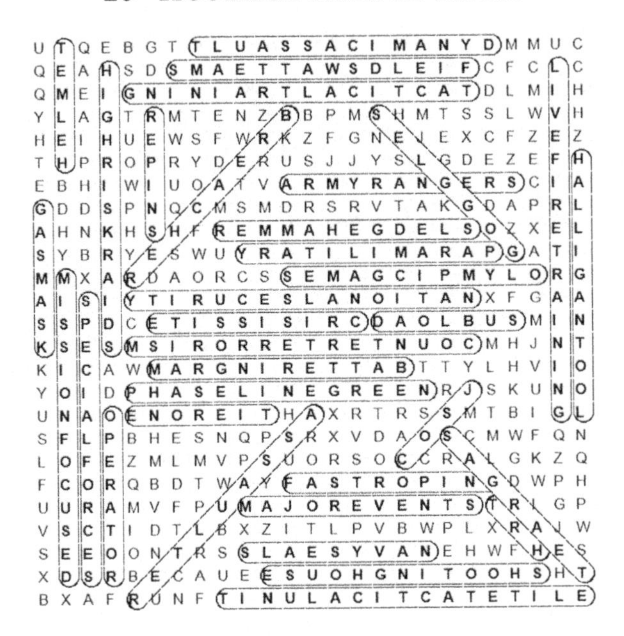

27 - INTERNATIONAL TERRORISM

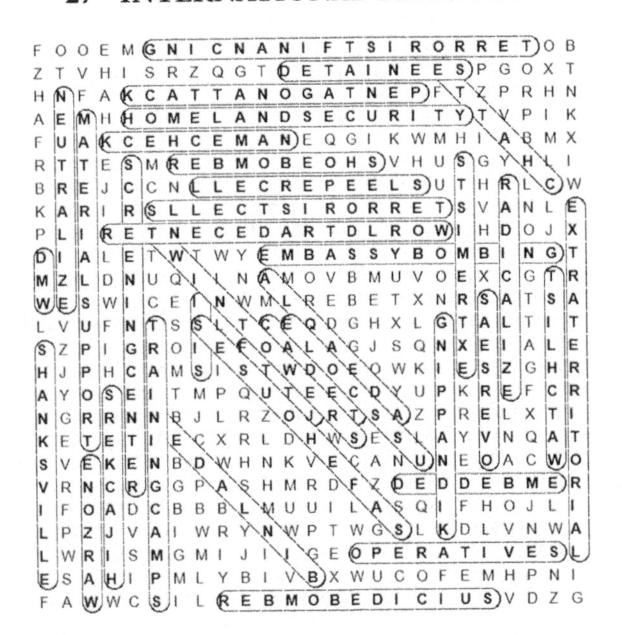

28 - DOMESTIC TERRORISM

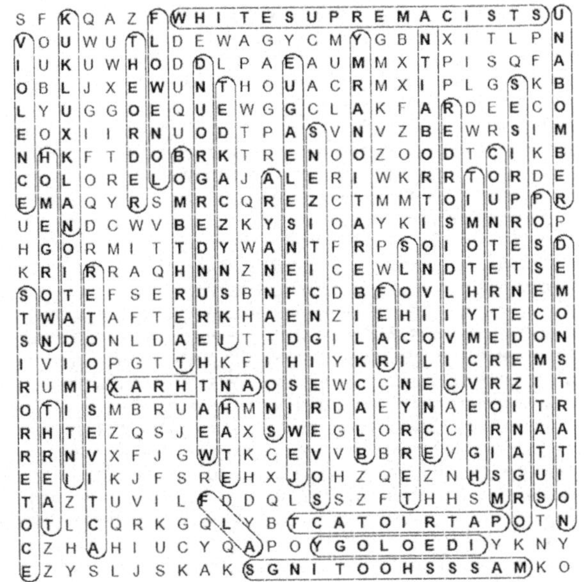

29 - CRISIS INCIDENT RESPONSE

```
T I N F O R M A T I O N S H A R I N G K S I W P F
N N S X L M J W Y B N D H F P M G N I S H S R C B
Z F T N T Z N U B B M A E T Y L F D E Q P E T T A
X C U O N T O D A D T V H M B M N N J F D B N R N
P F N S E M I U R O W C M O N A I S E N L O E O O
Y N O I M U T I R M M F E L P D T B A M W M M P I
S C K S Y N U O I W V P X P A N N M S A O B Y P T
J H K Y O A L P C O D U I E E E M L B S B D O U A
A I Z L L T O G A Z F N R M G O G G M S R O L S R
D P Z A P U S D D B G E S O C D U K K S E G P N U
A Z S N E R E H E S W S T T R U U Q C H P S E O G
I C C A D A R Z F F E I N R A E E C I O U B D I U
N M I L D L D F H S A E Q I L H T G R O S G S T A
T S P A I D G L S T D T S K L C T L G T H L A A N
E G M R P I F A O I P D H G Y Y Y Z X I B C E I I
R O Y O A S I R C H S C I T S I G O L N F S S V J
N D L I R A Y N K R O A D B L O C K S G K A R A O
A G O V J S L W H O S T A G E R E S C U E T E A M
T N N A M T A C T I V E S H O O T E R M G P V C L
I I R H T E A Y I N T E R M E D I A R I E S O P E
O K I E B R N J T A W S D E C N A H N E U H J E J
N C C B P U S L E E H W K L F S S U B B C O I S X
A A F L R F H U U M R J X L K I I I P M Q A W X A
L R R F G A R D B P R I S O N R I O T S O A B X J
Q T H E C N E L O I V E C A L P K R O W Q B W O H
```

30 - SIOC AND COMMAND CENTERS

```
C T J I C T L L Z R O K Y E B N S C P R Z L W E T
G M G M V I R T U A L C O M M A N D C E N T E R E
S V N O Z H F A S K Z G E Z C D O I I M V H W O L
E J I B V W Z A B P M N L G S O E U F W C E H P E
C Y S I M D E U J R V A E N Y Y B K O E N V G E C
U I S L M P X Z U O K Q C I W Y G Q T N O I F R O
R M E E C R E R T K C S T C B F W H S A H T H A M
E A C C O K C E R W I A R N B F G O L T S I V T M
T J O O M X U A A A Y T O E Q I A Y A I S S G I U
E O R M M K T L E B P E N R H W U L N O E N D O N
L R P M A L I T H Q C L I E N A X D I N N E E N I
E C N A N G V I T C P L C F L T I O M A I S T A C
P A O N D N E M F X W I L N L C O H R L D E N L A
H S I D P I B E O G W T I O A H M E E E A M E O T
O E T N O K R M E U F E B C W C P T T M E I I V I
N V A A S A I O T P P R R E O E Q Y R E R T R E O
E H M I T M E N A M L A A L E N S K E R F V O R N
S Q R I I N F I T L Y D R E D T C C T G O Y N S S
M I O D C O I T S C T I I T I E I R U E E K O I C
X X F B A I N O F W X O E G V R F N P N T H I G E
N M N R B S G R F K L S S D M P C N M C A D S H N
T P I R H I S I D K S Y M W Y O N J O I T L S T T
L K E Y T C B N V P D K P H I K D S C E S R I Z E
H B W T E E L G O I Y T M S O P V R O S D R M U R
Z A Y N W D L C I P F B S L L E C N O I S U F Z S
```

31 - SPECIAL AGENT BOMB TECH

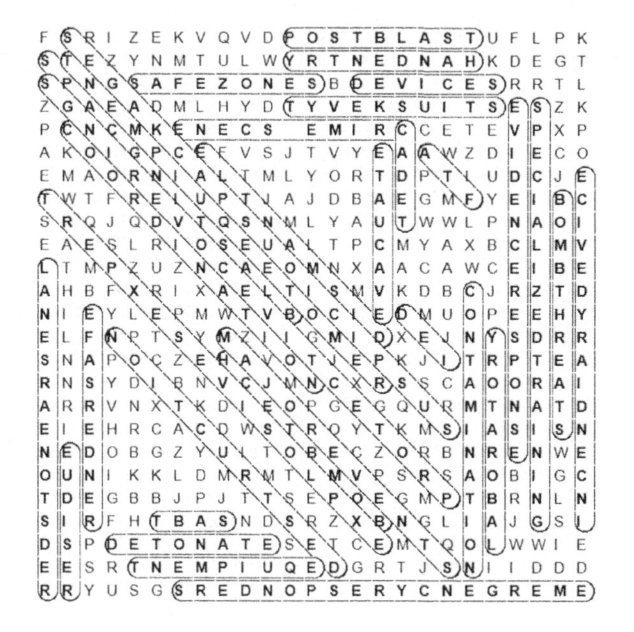

32 - WMD

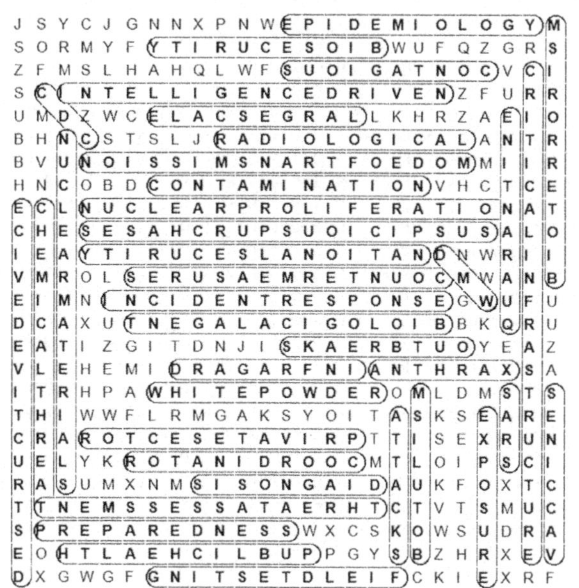

33 - FBI LABORATORY

J T R A C E E V I D E N C E J N I B Y T S G O D Y
S Z O C L P L O Y P A C B I L G P F S H N U E Q R
K S T N R E T T A P S D O O L B W V X G U Z B S Q
R I D N A T E S T I N G R R S I S Y L A N A J K R
A S S D K J H C S I E F F E C T M Z Q S E M N G Q
M Y F O R E N S I C S L A B D V E X G K S B P T A
L L I F D Z P V P X V I P U Q T V H N K G A N F F
O A D S U G S L C P U T G R I C I Z I C B N D O E
O N C M K V D G O R F T R W N B D Q T A L D N R J
T A Q H H O Y K D O A E A B W R E S S D S L Z E S
M C N T A V N R I D G S U I D K N R E Z S A M N T
A I C B I I N A S P C T S T C G C E T F E I S S N
X R S G V N N E S J V I M E E T E B C S N R C I I
E T R Y K U U O M G O M N M F E R I I R T D I C R
Y E A A Z K M Y F E T O R A K Y E F T T I N E P P
R M L Q E V L X R C S N K R Z Y S D S C W O N H T
A O P H T T L X E T U Y U K M S P N I E T H T O N
I I M Y N V A S P T S S X S P V O A L W R C I T E
T B E O C I P V M P K I T T T A N R L B E O S O T
N H X J Y M N N A D P B M O J O S I A G P T T G A
E F E O G V R I W C X W C E D N E A B L X I S R L
D V Y E Z I T A T S X D R E H Y T H W G E M C A G
I U Z T M Z V D B F T E T K W C E C E F V N Q P P
V I D H B O D I L Y F L U I D S A I J V O B W H C
E Y Q U E S T I O N E D D O C U M E N T S L G Y Q

34 - EVIDENCE RESPONSE TEAM 1

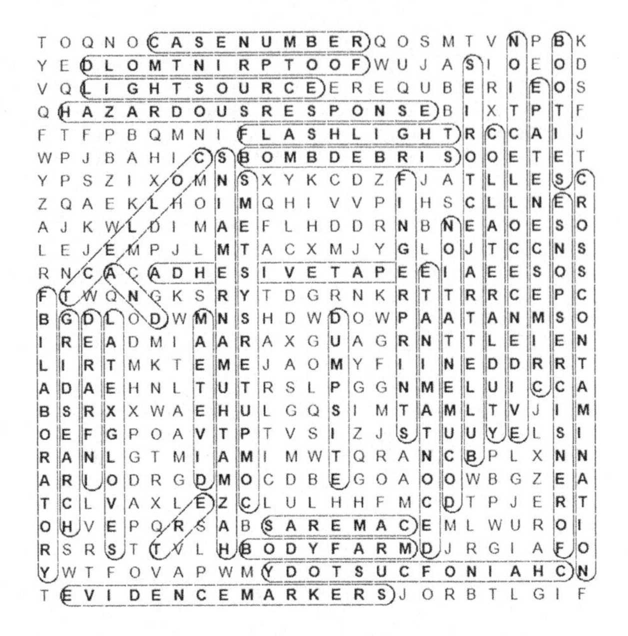

35 - EVIDENCE RESPONSE TEAM 2

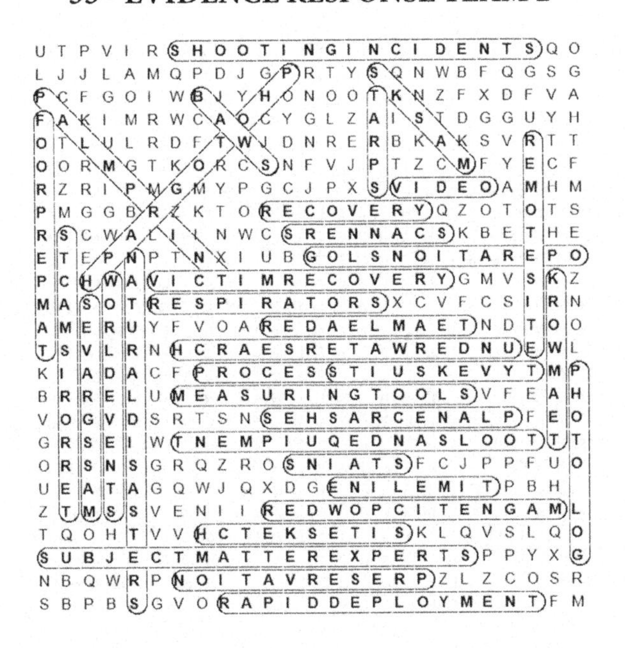

36 - MAJOR CASES

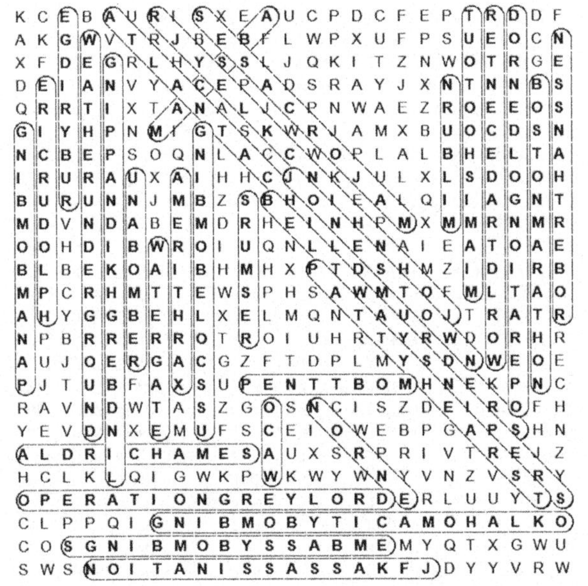

37 - ART THEFT

```
V K S L F G N I C N E F I N V E N T O R Y X U E U
K F J D N H G A R D N E R M U S E U M H W D O L S
W C I R R E T G R A V E P R O T E C T I O N H I F
R V T C V T N F N H G S H Z K N Z M W X J B Y F Y
H A R C H A E O L O G I C A L S I T E S Z R P T B
T I I P K C M X L F M T B E Z G Y B H J E E R R B
I N P R F I Y B O O D H E F W P L T H G G M I A U
E T H O J T O V R E T I K I C B T Z R G A V V N R
F E K V G N L V A S L S O O F L L O S E R A A E I
R R G E L E P A N A E T F R O O E D T E P R T L A
E S B N Z H E L T B X O S W O C O E C A Y T E O L
T T J A O T D U A A Y R W T N C M O D U T T C T S
N A H N P U D A R T H Y I I U I V U L C R H O S I
U T Y C V A I B T A E N W M R E F C O T E E L U T
O E O E D K P L I D G E E C R O E Q P I P F L E E
C T N M R Z A E F M X N T Y R K Y C R O O T E X S
A H P I Y P R S A Y T R W F W L T S E N R L C P E
U E R D E T S F C S A Z T G Z R P P T H P V T E L
Y F C O X B A N T I Q U I T I E S W N O N P I R U
R T V Y E N Y S S T X V A N F V U N I U E R O T G
E H C U L T U R A L P R O P E R T Y X S L A N V C
L Z E Y M A S T E R P I E C E S I H K E O L S I F
L V K I I E S M U E S U M X H F O E G H T Z J E Q
A C J A S R S E C U R I T Y S Y S T E M S P W R E
G V T S W T A V G O H A R T C O L L E C T O R S L
```

38 - CYBERCRIME

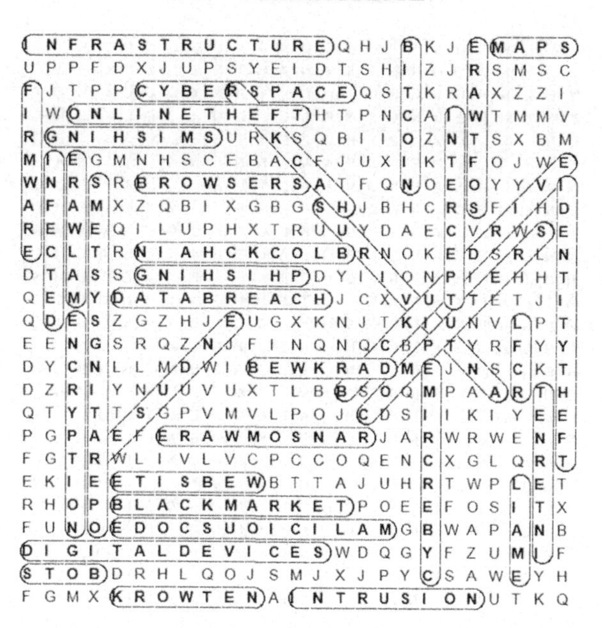

39 - CIVIL RIGHTS

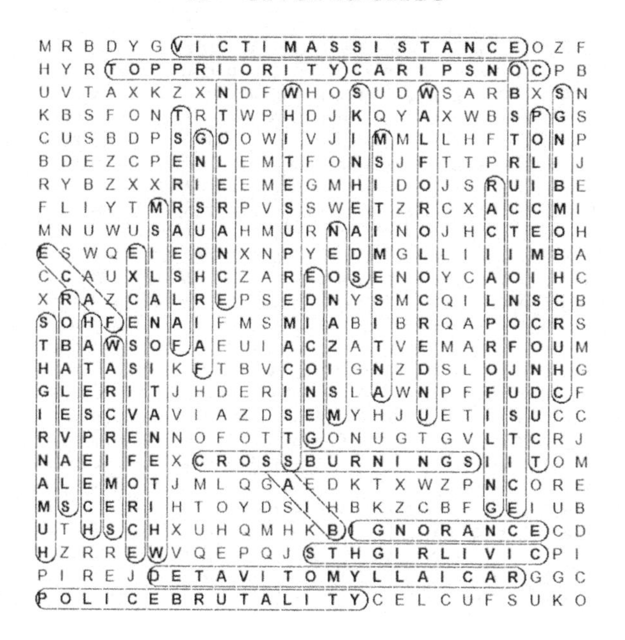

40 - COUNTERINTELLIGENCE

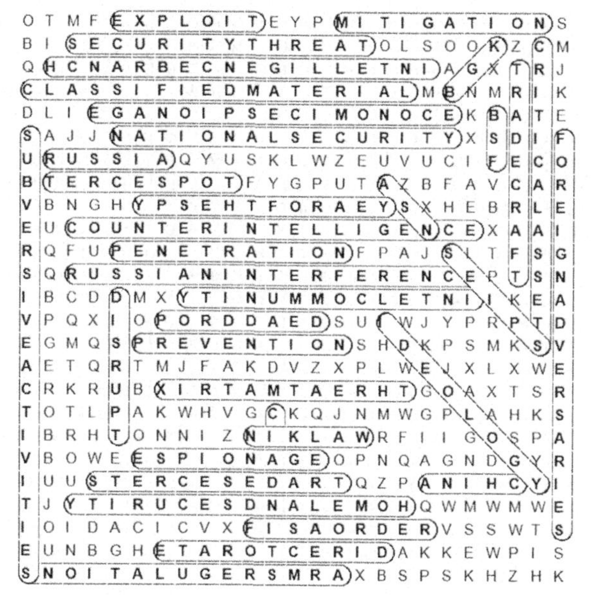

41 - AMERICAN SPIES

W G I W D U L T R U K E D W A R D S N O W D E N W
U B I S J G O R N E S S N A H T R E B O R U S H G
Y E L K A O Y O R O J I K K T V F X I I C I K C Z
E J N G R E B N E S O R S U I L U J B O L N Q R E
D L L S T E W A R T N O Z E T T E B L E A V G E R
Z I Y E C C H E L S E A M A N N I N G O Y W K K J
N A G E R N A I R B R Z A L T I Z H H H T J E L C
E N O O B D I V A D I L H R R N S S V X O I N A H
F F Y Y R J A B C R G I R E C O E D O U N V S W R
S N C U R R F V R E S O L K N R L A N D L A E N I
H O T E U N Y Z R H B L P E I E A R Y A O T U H S
A T Z X P X S H Z E I Q T X H H J N T N N O Q O T
R L B R F D I N R M S H Y H C C N O R A E G U J O
O E Q Z M S X T D G E M A V I S N C A M T U D V P
N P X F S G L R O L M D S R A A B E M O R R K N H
S D D U E I A E R T A Y M F T M F E M N E I C U E
C L I I P H U O Y Q H Q A N U O Z L I T E D I I R
R A Z K C U S R U M C C R C W D C E S E U A R T B
A N A I K E I G K P I R D A Y R S D K S D Q E J O
N O R W N B G S L D R M O S R A W Y A H O U D T Y
A R O B U R G V I I D B R B R N Q L M D L I E V C
G L E C Y E H P Y K L Q M Y A O N C Z I I N R Q E
E R J G N E Q U L S A J V R L E K B H F X O F V W
G A B O E A R L P I T T S N O L R Q J Y I S S W Z
Z L R K Q J O N A T H A N P O L L A R D H E R Q F

42 - NCIC DATABASE

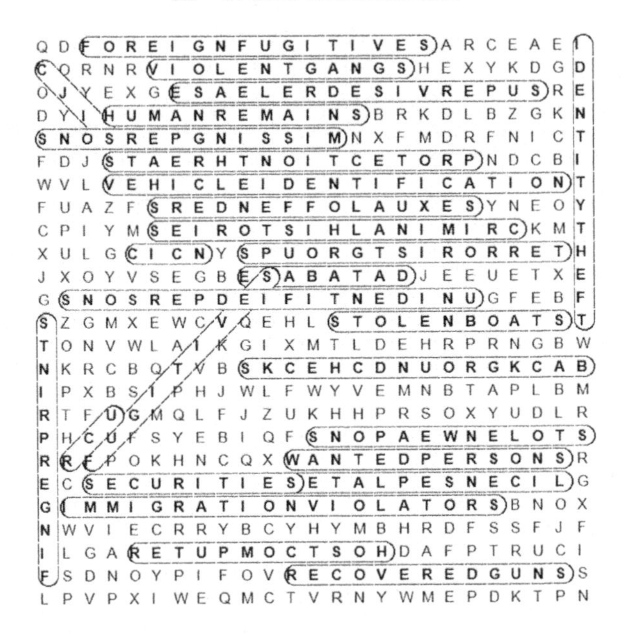

43 - CRIMES AGAINST CHILDREN

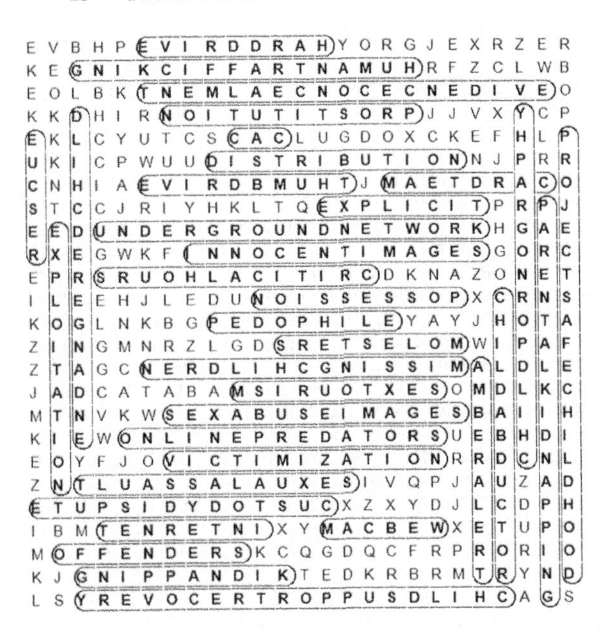

44 - ORGANIZED CRIME LCN

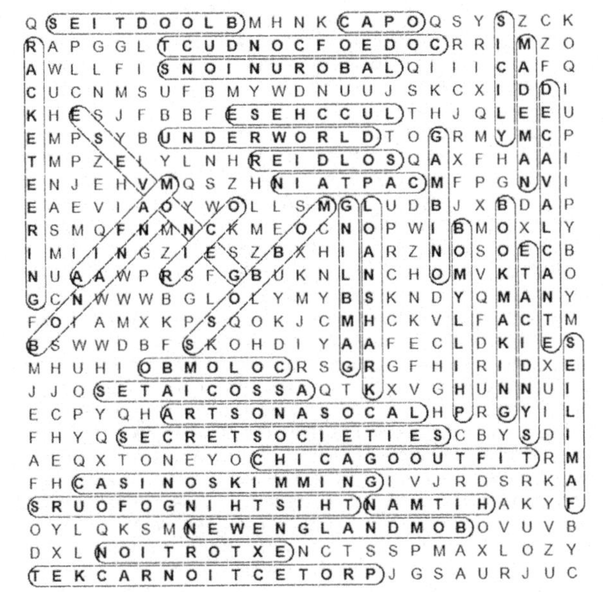

45 - ORGANIZED CRIME (TRANS)

```
R I C O A C T P Q I C Y B E R C R I M E S Z Y Q A
K T U H Z J Z D R U G T R A F F I C K I N G C L X
W Q Y R E B I R B N S N N T E K R A M K C A L B T
S P H S G N A G N A C I R E M A L A R T N E C M F
D I S R U P T S F R S H C R A G I L O E F G W I E
S E I R T N U O C N E V A H E F A S N S S T P D H
S E X M T S V A F R I C A R N R O S O R M X R D T
M B T I T E K U C E B C Q K R X U T I O P S E L T
O A D G C S C R I M E F A M I L Y Q T H G D D E R
N A J R R I S S G Z W R G B A C W E P U S A I E A
E I W A I R Q F A I P L N L W O C O U M N I C A R
Y S Q N M P C T R Y F V I A X U Z B R A A R A S N
L A R T I R F P E T A G R Y N N P I R N L T T T A
A U A S N E R O T I C W E R C T R B O T C G E G M
U N N M A T A B T R S A E E M E O D C R N N O D E
N N S U L N U E E U A L T V C R S D P A A O F S Q
D O O G I E D Z S C G N E A U F T I A F K K F R D
E I M G Z B S U M E A I K L E E I S Q F L G E H P
R T W L E Z C U U S M S C S P I T M G I A N N K Q
I R A I D I H C G R B E A Z O T U A L C B O S P K
N O R N T Q E O G E L V R F R G T N D K D H E O U
G T E G O W M T L D I E X J U O I T O I X R S V S
B X A N N L E Z I R N I A L E O O L V N G M S R X
S E N W G B S R N O G H Z I A D N E T G Q X C J E
X H T S S I Z O G B I T Q V N S D A R K W E B L P
```

46 – ARREST/SEARCH WARRANTS

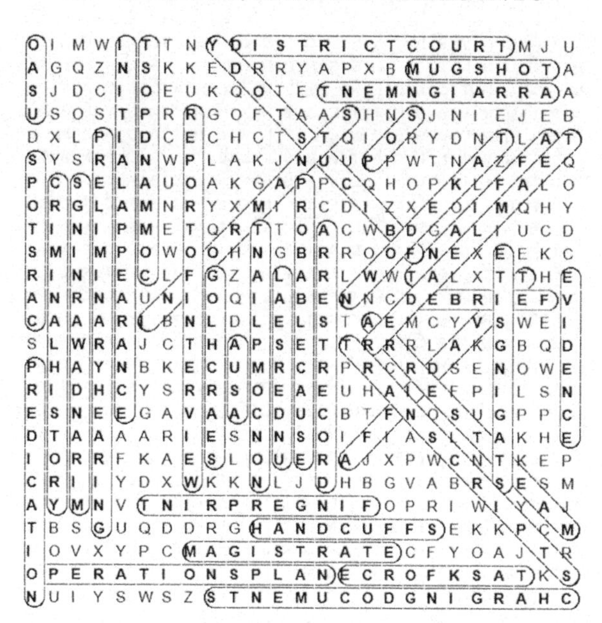

47 – TRIALS/COURT PROCEEDINGS

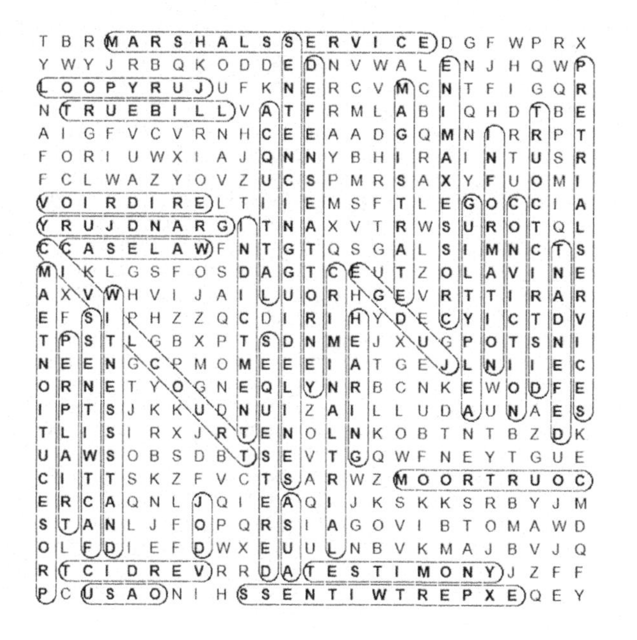

48 - RADIO ALPHABET

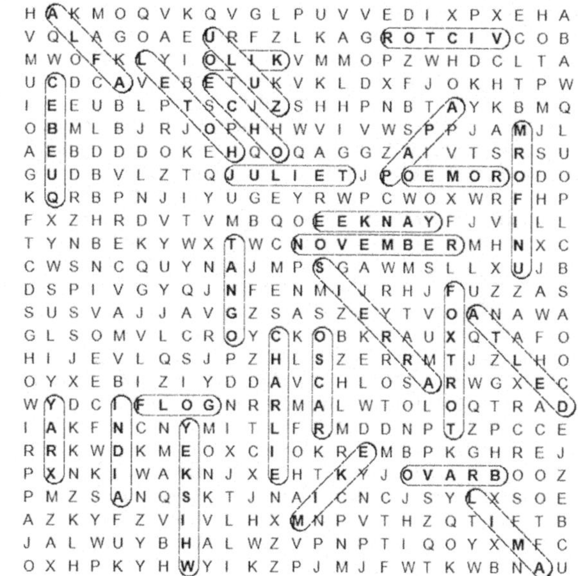

49 - CASE MANAGEMENT

O Y W E I V R E T N I F O T R O P E R Q A V I Z T
R E P O S I T O R I E S U U R C S D A E L F I D S
U E X B N T C A D E R Y T P N I D E N I L D A E D
Q A E I M M E D I A T E Z V N X E D D G S Y L J G
Q M M H R D W S O R N O I T I S O P S I D X E P O
Y Q F R E T N E C A T A D O L L E T A C O P N E F
B N N F I T P U T N E M E G A N A M E S A C I N I
A W P R E L I M I N A R Y I N Q U I R Y P E T D L
I U E A P N L R E A D I N G R O O M Y R E N N I E
G S D H G C F A T A D A T E M Q A U H P L I E N N
I C E I S S E C O R P L A V O R P P A Y E T S G U
Y Y A A B N X B C E T I S B E W T E T A C U D I M
E Y S S R L N A R L Q R T L U A V E H T T O I N B
C S R K E C E Q I Z A V D B F Y W R I Z R R G A E
N Y A A C F H R U R I S W F N L Z M X R O K I C R
E Q D C R E I A E E E N S U H F Q T H O N I T T M
D N I B D B H L B C R C Y I D A Q C A B I N A I G
E F Y Y D E I C E L O Y O K F H P N N C C D L V A
C F T S A Y S L E I E R S R Q I H I Y S R E C E F
E Y I A K L U O O M E P D H D L E J O W E X O P D
R K R E J J Z R L D A R H J T S N D J F C S P F N
P G O E H V I E O C S N P T J X U O V V O K I U X
O G I X Y B B H L I N K A N A L Y S I S R T E B R
H E R L J U F D I S S E M I N A T E F P D T S U F
Q R P U G H G W S N X D E N N A C S A I D E M C P

50 - LEGAL ATTACHE PROGRAM

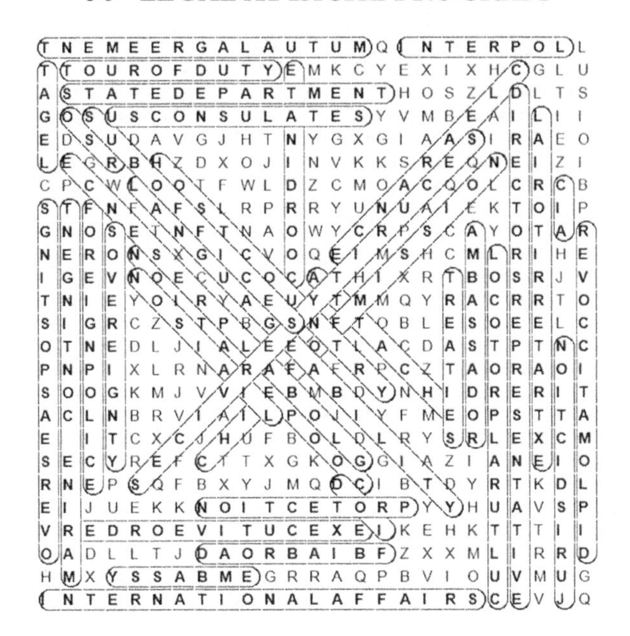

51 - OVERSEAS OFFICES (A-K)

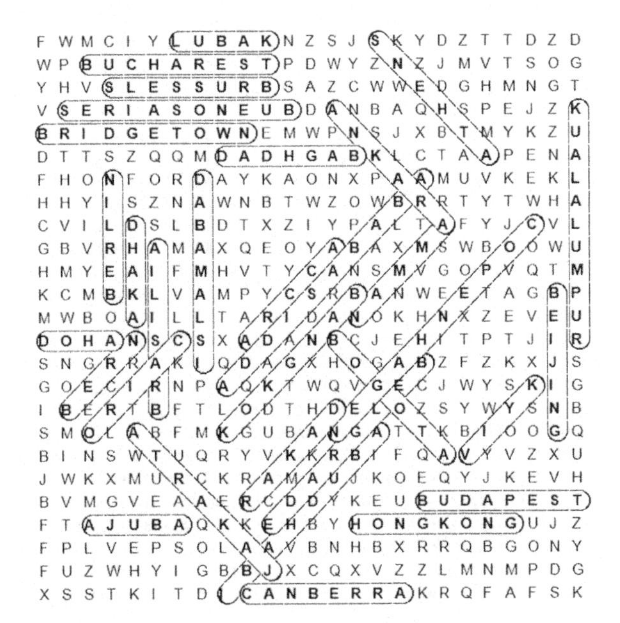

52 - OVERSEAS OFFICES (L-Z)

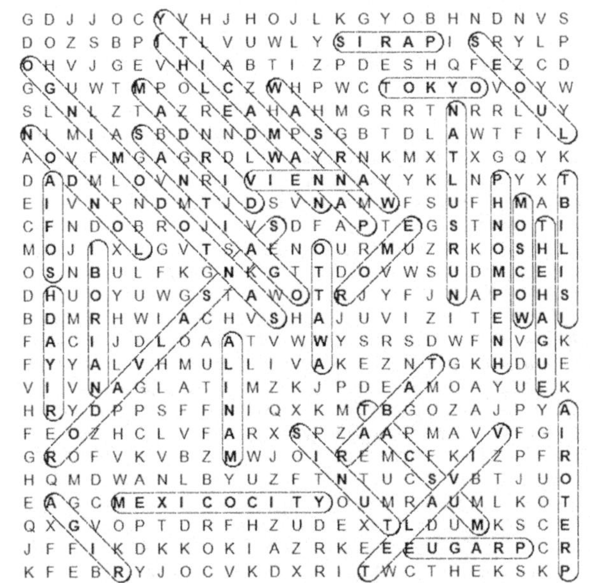

53 - LANGUAGE ANALYSTS

S T Q C T Z W C C U L T U R A L E X P E R T I S E
Y E R W A Y G N I D A E R T W F H S E M T P J N S
Z K I A R C R C A F L O N V N N H Q A N W E U C S
M G K T N G O X V U A G L H P V O I J L G Z S Q F
L C L X I S V N E X M I N N D T F P P G V L R T M
R A I O T N L M T S V X C I P C Y W Z F M C I H S
C U S L B S U A F R E W P X N Y K S O L W A T S X
T V E S R A K T T P A M R V T E P A S H T O P E H
S V G G O Z L Q R E R C A J H Q T D H N H L N K Y
E S A H T G U S K O D O T N K U C S C D S I A R S
T T U X A N C C O J P O F L T U R Q I G I B E V N
E P G N L I K P Q C C P C I I E H O B L N D R B A
G I N L S N D J P J I H O U C N I Y A O A X O Z I
A R A G N E A R M W G E I L M I G V R E P N K B S
U C L N A E H X W L N R T N E E E U A G S K P K S
G S L X R R E U D G I Y B Y E V N N I X N J H T U
N N A E T C V W S J K U R D U S A T C S G K J R R
A A C G B S O T H J A P A N E S E R F Y T F Z M D
L R I F U N A T I V E S P E A K E R T N R S S F C
U T T S K Y Q E T U P C C A S L L I K S T H Z Z F
T Q I D F K Y T W X S B G C Z R D D M H L S Y S P
X U R Y E C A R E E R O P P O R T U N I T I E S D
F G C O V E R S E A S A S S I G N M E N T F D F O
Y R A T I N G I D N G I E R O F F A R S I T A P A
S W Z N A P Y Q V G N I T E R P R E T N I L Y W H

54 - FINGERPRINT IDENT

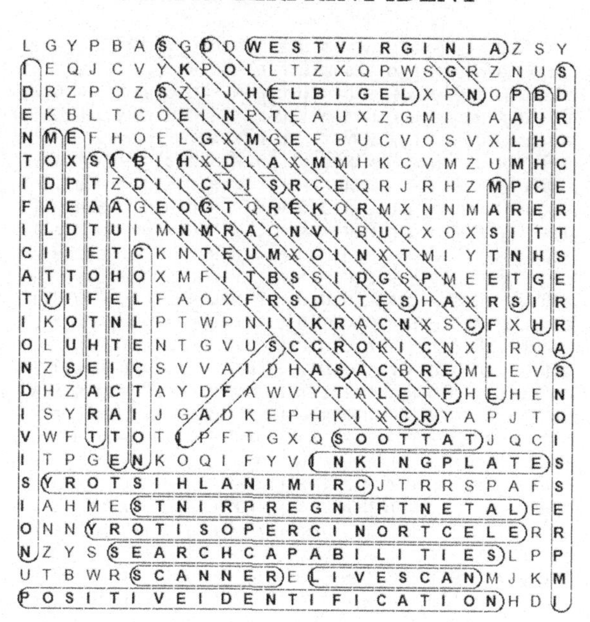

55 - FBI DIRECTORS

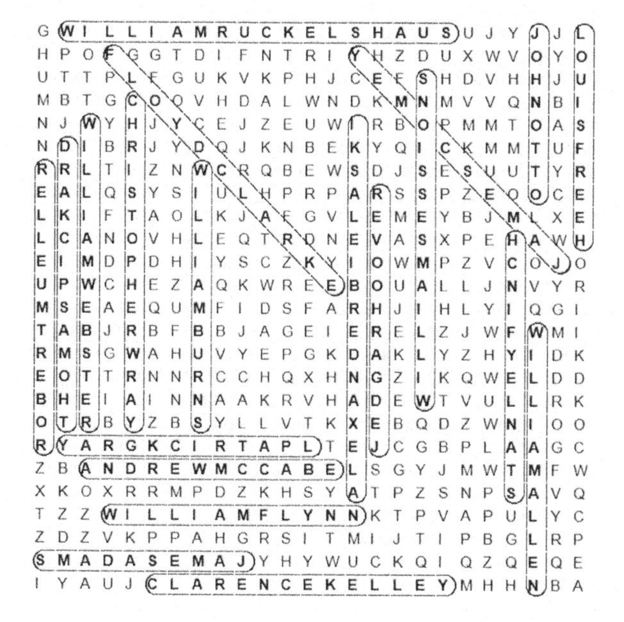

56 - INFAMOUS BAD GUYS

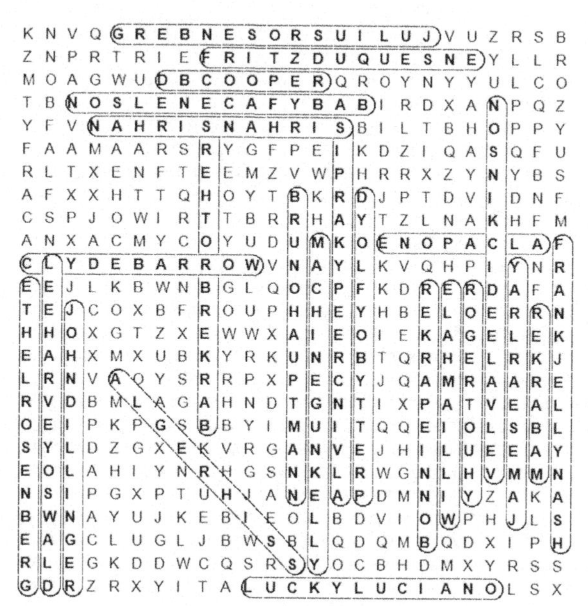

57 - UNDERCOVER AGENTS

```
U Y G C J R S H O W M O N E Y F C O V E R T I B V
I F R G N I P P O T S K C A B B D P C L L K E L S
J Y O M Y U C A R E D R O C E R Y D O B O G F U G
T N U I N D R O Q S A W T Q I T C Q E W W D I Q D
R R P F D C E D E W Y T I L I B A T I U S L L D U
O K   K C O N V C M N O I T A R E P O G N I T S K
P S I P W B P R T D A Z H I I C S C E C V C E J B
P M P K W S U N D E R C O V E R S C H O O L R P E
U S Z E F Y U Q O I R A N E C S N C J U L N C T T
S B C N C I J O Y F W N D I M P R O V I S E E B A
L C I S F I S Z R S L L A R E V O C P E E D S Y R
A U U F R S A O R E D R O C E R L A T I G I D Y T
C A C L W O E L L S G T N E M N G I S S A S W T L
I C O C S O T K T A E N E I T F Y I G O T M I I I
G N A L O R A A A Y T N A T O A C G O I N R S T F
O O M S M O O R L T T E S D W W S Q V R E E E N N
L I F Y E R R T T U S R D I N I S P F V G T G E I
O T U F U A E D A X P H A C T H E T W T A T U D U
H C Y Z S W G T I I L I G N X I R Q R Z T R Y I F
C A V R M I S E G N T Y N I S O V Z O S C O G E S
Y R L N S F T I N N A O J A H F L E B H A H X S A
S T D Y R V U E N T O T G W M W E R B Q T S A L A
P X C H E D S F E D N L O E B N L R D F N O I A F
Q E S A F E T Y C O N C E R N S R H U O O N B F C
T N O I T A N O S R E P M I M R W O R U C N S C B
```

58 - HUMAN INTELLIGENCE

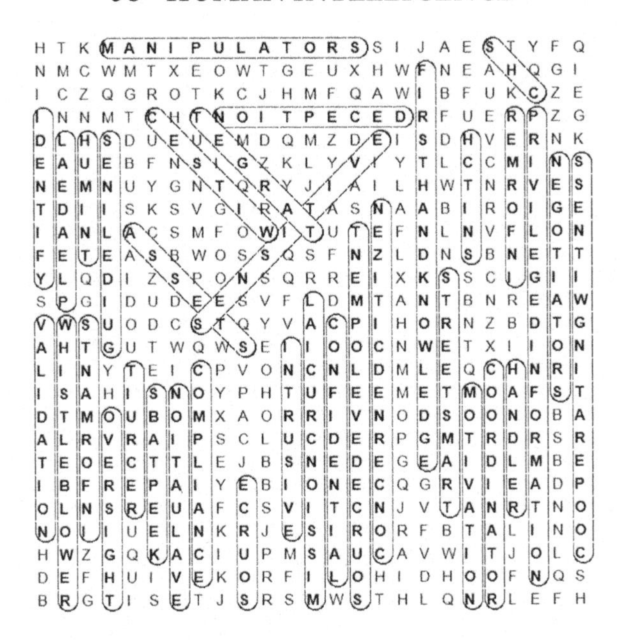

59 - VIOLENT GANGS

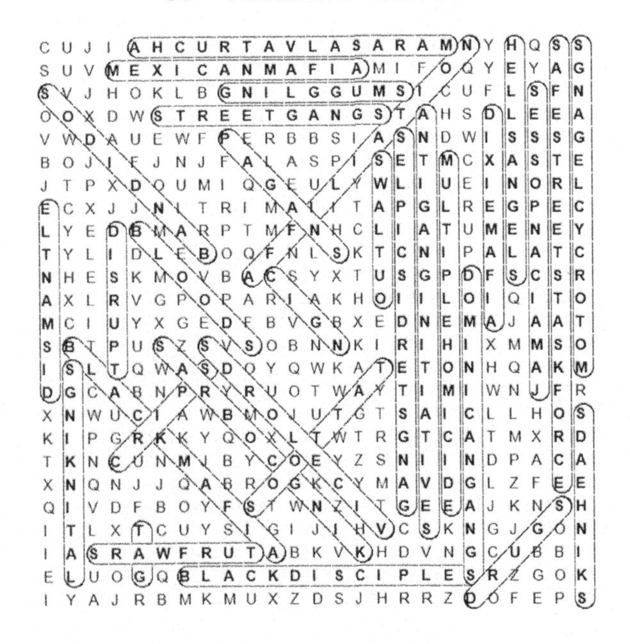

60 - DRUG TRAFFICKING

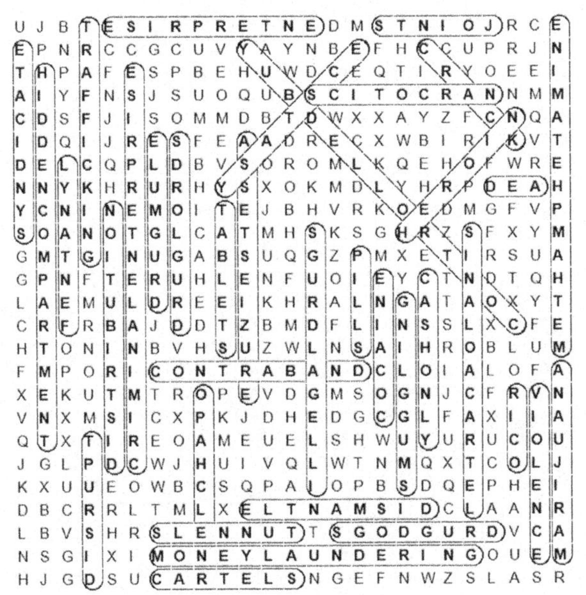

61 - BANK ROBBERY

T M C A N L A T E N T F I N G E R P R I N T S X P
A S B C B E H J F G P B A N K N O T E E T L M W L
R Z D E S C R I P T I O N A F F S M F P C L E X M
Z T I E A F G S D F E D E R A L L Y I N S U R E D
X W S U R V E I L L A N C E C A M E R A S J L K H
R C G Q R J N W J U Z O X C A S H I E R L C V F I
U Q L K H M R E Y W P H O T O S P R E A D C S S J
V G C X X Z F E N F C L X Z J A Q J H B B Q S L B
R T W H V D U Z M E L C I H E V H C T I W S A L D
K R T Z I Y T S R E M O T S U C M I T C I V V I E
M S Z C N R C R R E S I U G S I D C R F N L N B M
X L E B V R E U B S T P I B Y Q E S K O S M A D A
S M U R D R Z K K H D J T Z K E U Z Z Z O O C E N
B R R I I W A X C I X D R T W N N S H D E D D K D
D A Y E X A X C H A Y D J Z G L K O U M M E O R N
T L N X L M L Y Y E R U Q L T U P S M U T A O A O
I A U K H L B N P A Q T A B Z X O L R T R F H M T
P T E Z M L E A U V W S S C D P W P A M I D R Y E
S N K K E A C T A M S A F P E U B B O N K A O N J
T E E B D K N Q K E B F T R G M I R A N Y U B H A
E L Y A U D S A S N N E A E X E E P R V K W H W Q
R I V E V S J D G V A N R Q G D T S I E H Q G G R
L S X J H A N P Z E D B P S C D E B E R J O I Q F
Y R T O O L J U T L R U J A W M V S P Q L J E H U
L H P N T A K E O V E R R O B B E R Y X O B N V U

62 - HALL OF HONOR - 1

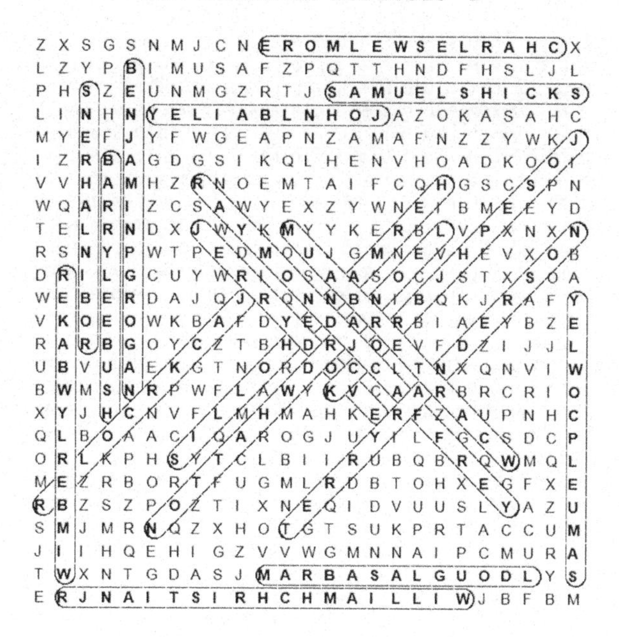

63 - HALL OF HONOR – 2

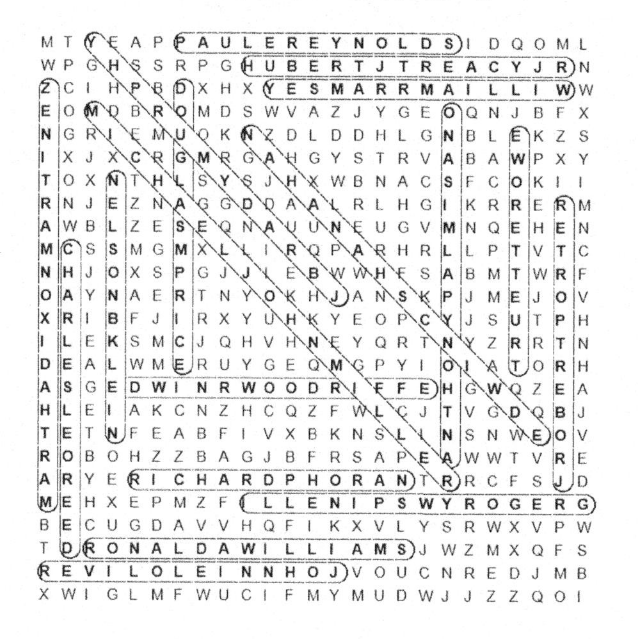

64 - FUGITIVES

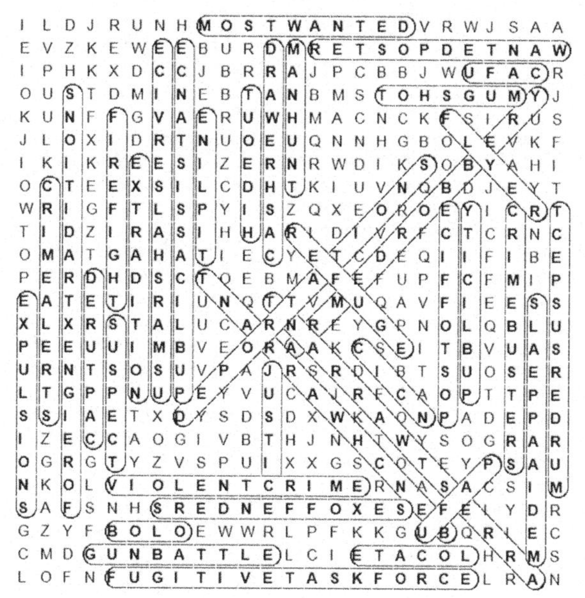

65 – KIDNAPPING

```
G N I D N U F T S I R O R R E T P L P Z F J Q E A
A E C N A R A E P P A S I D T Z A G K G S U H U W
R O T A I T O G E N T R W E F O R V G K T F R D L
C N N V X Z B C C Q E U C S E R E Y M I E M I H E
D H R M A N H U N T I E R C P L N T I D R S S S O
R C H I L D A B D U C T I O N K T L S N V A R T J
E Q N D W V S X R X K I T J T Q A B S A Y E O A D
T P Z U S I F H E O C B P U Y Z L U I P E S T T R
T U H N L C D O D L O E Y R K B K D N P T R A E O
E B I D N T E S R R L M R I U U I P G E O E R P P
L L O E Y I N T U F C I K S L R D G P R N V I R O
N I D R J M I A M J G R P D I I N K E A M O P O F
E C A G B S A G Q L N C B I N E A L R Z O J S S F
T A E R V P R E X J I T V C S D P G S S S L N E A
T P D O U E T T M U K N Z T T A P F O B N Z O C R
I P D U S C S A H I C E L I R L I U N A A D C U E
R E E N R I E K P I I L P O U I N Q S E R X O T A
W A M D O A R I K J T O H N C V G Y C W N I C I V
D L U B T L X N F S S I M Z T E E X T O R T I O N
N S S U P I R G T O J V K I I R E C O V E R Y N B
A U E N A S I Z A T G U N P O I N T G L W T N I T
H R R K C T I I B N O S C R N T D J D S B N E Y O
A G P E U S P I P Z Y V L R S P I P M B K E X E F
W H S R P E T A T S R E T N I Y K E G E X S V Y I
P R O O F O F L I F E U N M A R K E D B I L L S N
```

66 - MAJOR THEFT

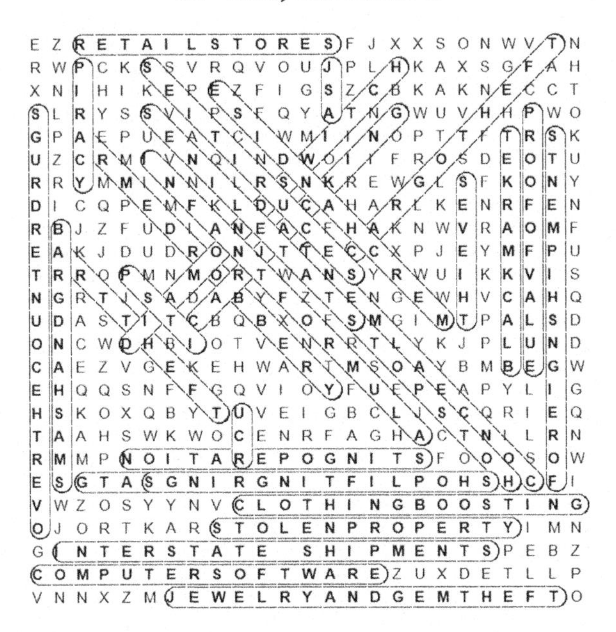

67 - LAW ENFORCEMENT PARTNERS

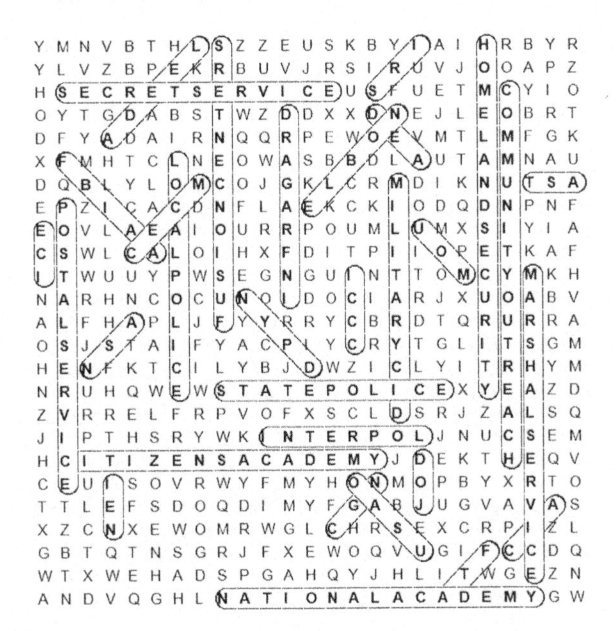

68 - FBI VOCABULARY – 1

1. l
2. j
3. g
4. c (Be On the Lookout)
5. b (Bureau Deadline)
6. f (Close of Business)
7. k (Cover Your A**)
8. I (Frigging New Guy)
9. e (Kiss My A**)
10. h (Personally Owned Vehicle)
11. d (Regular Day Off)
12. a (Unknown Subject)

69 - FBI VOCABULARY – 2

1. g
2. b
3. i
4. k
5. c
6. h
7. d
8. f
9. j (Cooperating Witness)
10. e
11. l (Title 3)
12. a (Wild A** Guess)

70 - FBI VOCABULARY – 3

1. d
2. c
3. b
4. e (Confidential Informant)
5. k
6. j
7. l (First Name Unknown – Last Name Unknown)
8. i
9. h
10. a
11. g
12. f

71 - FBI VOCABULARY – 4

1. d
2. i
3. a
4. l
5. f
6. h
7. j
8. c (Personally Owned Weapon)
9. e
10. k
11. g
12. b

THANK YOU!

I hope you enjoyed ***FBI Word Search Puzzles: Fun for Armchair Detectives***. Please take a moment to post a short review on the online retailer where you purchased the book. Reviews help readers find good books.

Please visit **jerriwilliams.com** to join my Reader Team and receive the FBI Reading Resource, a colorful list of books about the FBI written by FBI agents; the printable FBI Reality Checklist; updates on the FBI in books, TV, and movies; and more via my monthly email digest!

OTHER BOOKS BY JERRI WILLIAMS

Available as ebooks, paperbacks, and audiobooks wherever books are sold:

FBI Myths and Misconceptions: A Manual for Armchair Detectives

Pay To Play (Philadelphia FBI Corruption Squad Book 1)

Greedy Givers (Philadelphia FBI Corruption Squad Book 2)

Spoiled Sport (Philadelphia FBI Corruption Squad Book 3 - Coming Soon)

Made in United States
Orlando, FL
14 February 2023